INTRODUCTION TO ABSTRACT ALGEBRA

BY

C. R. J. CLAPHAM

D1613090

LONDON: Routledge & Kegan Paul Ltd
NEW YORK: Dover Publications Inc

First Published 1969
in Great Britain by
Routledge & Kegan Paul Ltd
Broadway House, 68–74 Carter Lane
London, EC4V 5EL
and in the U.S.A. by
Dover Publications Inc.
180 Varick Street
New York, 10014
Reprinted 1974

ISBN 0 7100 6626 0

Printed in Great Britain
by Unwin Brothers Limited
The Gresham Press, Old Woking, Surrey
A member of the Staples Printing Group

Preface

In this book, I have aimed to provide a simple introduction to some of the important concepts of modern algebra: integral domains, fields, rings, vector spaces and field extensions. The theory of groups is not included, but is covered in the volume *Sets and Groups* by J. A. Green, in this Library, and the development here assumes no knowledge of groups. The reader who is familiar with group theory, however, will recognize many situations and analogies without having them pointed out to him.

The whole account is straightforward and is written for those who are making their first encounter with abstract algebra. The final chapter on field extensions uses many of the results developed earlier in the book and concludes with a proof of the impossibility of various constructions with ruler and compasses.

I should like to record here my thanks to Professor Walter Ledermann who read an early draft of this book and made several valuable suggestions. I am also grateful to Dr. Brian Rotman for his helpful comments upon the manuscript.

The University of Aberdeen   C. R. J. CLAPHAM

Contents

CHAPTER ONE

Integral Domains

1. Introduction

We are going to begin by studying the integers and proving various results about them, some of which will be very familiar, others not so familiar. In order to establish theorems about the properties of the integers, we must agree on certain facts about them of which we do not require proof, and from these **postulates,** as they are called, all other results are to be deduced. We shall be careful to assume nothing except the postulates that have been chosen.

First, let us fix some notation that will be used throughout this book:

J denotes the set of all integers, i.e. the positive integers 1, 2, 3, ..., the negative integers -1, -2, -3 ..., and zero 0.

Q denotes the set of all rational numbers, i.e. all numbers which can be written as fractions m/n, where m, n are integers and $n \neq 0$.

R denotes the set of all real numbers. This includes numbers such as 0, $\frac{1}{2}$, -3, $\sqrt{2}$, 4·75, π. Some of these cannot be written as fractions but they all have an expansion as an infinite decimal.

C denotes the set of all complex numbers. These are usually written in the form $a + bi$, where a, b are real and $i = \sqrt{(-1)}$.

2. Operations

We are familiar with addition, subtraction and multiplication of numbers and these are three examples of **operations.** An operation ○ is a rule which associates with two elements a and b, an element denoted by $a \circ b$.

DEFINITION. *A set S is* **closed under the operation** ○ *if, for any two elements a and b in S, there is defined uniquely an element of S denoted by* $a \circ b$.

Example 1. **J**, **Q**, **R** and **C** are each closed under the operations of addition, subtraction and multiplication. None of these sets, however, is closed under division, for if we take $b = 0$, $a \div b$ is not defined. The set of *positive* real numbers is closed under division, for $a \div b$ is a well-defined positive real number for any a and b. The set of positive integers is not closed under subtraction: if $a < b$, $a - b$ is not a positive integer.

Example 2. An operation need not be between numbers. If A and B are sets, the **intersection** $A \cap B$ of A and B is the set of all elements which belong to both A and B. The **union** $A \cup B$ of A and B is the set of all elements of A together with all elements of B. Then $\cap$ and $\cup$ are operations.

3. Definition of an Integral Domain

Now we take certain postulates about addition and multiplication which hold not only for **J** but also for other sets of numbers such as **Q**, **R** and **C**. There may also be other sets, whose elements are not numbers, that satisfy these postulates. A set with two operations with these properties is given a special name:

DEFINITION. *A set D is an* **integral domain** *if D is closed under two operations, called addition and multiplication and denoted in the usual way,*† *with these properties:*

1. *For all a, b, c in D,* $a + (b + c) = (a + b) + c$. (*Addition is* **associative**.)

2. *For all a, b in D,* $a + b = b + a$. (*Addition is* **commutative**.)

3. *There is an element* 0 *in D such that* $a + 0 = a$ *for all a in D.* (*There is a* **zero** *element.*)

4. *For each a in D, there is an element* $(-a)$ *such that* $a + (-a) = 0$. (Each element has a **negative**.)

---

† In this book, we shall keep to the convention of denoting the operation of multiplication by . but normally writing ab instead of $a.b$.

2

DEFINITION OF AN INTEGRAL DOMAIN

5. *For all a, b, c in D, a(bc) = (ab)c. (Multiplication is associative.)*
6. *For all a, b in D, ab = ba. (Multiplication is commutative.)*
7. *There is a non-zero element 1 in D such that a1 = a for all a in D. (There is an **identity** element.)*
8. *For all a, b, c in D, a(b + c) = ab + ac*
   and (a + b)c = ac + bc.
   *(Multiplication is **distributive** over addition.)*
9. *For all a, b in D, ab = 0 only if a = 0 or b = 0.*

If in a set closed under addition and multiplication satisfying at least **1, 2, 3, 4, 5, 8**†, there are non-zero elements a, b such that $ab = 0$, then a and b are called **divisors of zero**. So **9** says that there are no divisors of zero in an integral domain. Notice that **8** consists of two distributive laws, but one of them follows from the other if multiplication is commutative.

Example 3. A **2 x 2 real matrix** is an array of four real numbers p, q, r, s arranged like this $\begin{pmatrix} p & q \\ r & s \end{pmatrix}$. Two such matrices can be added and multiplied according to the following rules

$$\begin{pmatrix} p & q \\ r & s \end{pmatrix} + \begin{pmatrix} x & y \\ z & t \end{pmatrix} = \begin{pmatrix} p + x & q + y \\ r + z & s + t \end{pmatrix},$$

$$\begin{pmatrix} p & q \\ r & s \end{pmatrix}\begin{pmatrix} x & y \\ z & t \end{pmatrix} = \begin{pmatrix} px + qz & py + qt \\ rx + sz & ry + st \end{pmatrix}.$$

The reader may check that the set of all 2×2 real matrices satisfies **1, 2, 3, 4, 5, 7, 8**. The zero element required in **3**, and the identity element required in **7** are respectively

$$\mathbf{O} = \begin{pmatrix} 0 & 0 \\ 0 & 0 \end{pmatrix} \text{ and } \mathbf{I} = \begin{pmatrix} 1 & 0 \\ 0 & 1 \end{pmatrix}.$$

That **6** is not satisfied may be seen by choosing, for example,

$$\mathbf{A} = \begin{pmatrix} 0 & 1 \\ 0 & 0 \end{pmatrix} \text{ and } \mathbf{B} = \begin{pmatrix} 1 & 0 \\ 0 & 0 \end{pmatrix},$$

for then

$$\mathbf{AB} = \begin{pmatrix} 0 & 0 \\ 0 & 0 \end{pmatrix} \text{ and } \mathbf{BA} = \begin{pmatrix} 0 & 1 \\ 0 & 0 \end{pmatrix}.$$

So $\mathbf{AB} \neq \mathbf{BA}$. Moreover, these two matrices are divisors of zero, since $\mathbf{AB} = \mathbf{O}$ with neither $\mathbf{A} = \mathbf{O}$ nor $\mathbf{B} = \mathbf{O}$.

† This is the definition of a *ring*. Rings will be studied in Chapter 5.

INTEGRAL DOMAINS

4. Elementary Properties

It is taken for granted that the integers as we know them satisfy the necessary properties for an integral domain, just as we shall assume that the sets **Q, R** and **C** satisfy the definition. But from **1** to **9** we can prove many elementary consequences which must therefore hold in any integral domain. They will be results we know very well to be true for ordinary numbers.

THEOREM 1. *In any integral domain*
(i) *there is a unique zero element,*
(ii) *there is a unique identity element,*
(iii) *each element has a unique negative.*

Proof. (i) Suppose that 0_1 and 0_2 both have the property stated in **3**. Then $0_2 + 0_1 = 0_2$, because 0_1 is a zero element, and $0_1 + 0_2 = 0_1$, because 0_2 is a zero element. But $0_1 + 0_2 = 0_2 + 0_1$, by **2**, so $0_1 = 0_2$. (ii) is proved similarly.

(iii) Suppose that b and c are both the negative of a. Then $a + b = 0$ and $a + c = 0$. So $b + (a + c) = b + 0 = b$, by **3**. But also $b + (a + c) = (b + a) + c$ (by **1**) $= (a + b) + c$ (by **2**) $= 0 + c = c + 0$ (by **2**) $= c$ (by **3**). Therefore $b = c$.

We may now agree to write $a - b$ instead of $a + (-b)$, for subtraction is not a new operation but can be defined from addition and the existence of the negative of every element.

THEOREM 2. *In any integral domain D*
(i) $-(-a) = a$, *for all a in D,*
(ii) $a - b = 0$ *if and only if $a = b$, for all a, b in D,*
(iii) $a0 = 0$, *for all a in D,*
(iv) $-(ab) = a(-b) = (-a)b$, *for all a, b in D,*
(v) $(-a)(-b) = ab$, *for all a, b in D,*
(vi) $(-1)a = (-a)$, *for all a in D.*
(vii) $ab = ac$ *only if either $a = 0$ or $b = c$. (The* **Cancellation Law***).*

4

Proof. (i) $(-a) + a = a + (-a)$ (by **2**) $= 0$ (by **4**). Thus a has the property required of the negative of $(-a)$. So $a = -(-a)$.

(ii) If $a = b$, then $a - b = a + (-b) = b + (-b) = 0$. Conversely, if $a - b = 0$, then $a + (-b) = 0$. So $(a + (-b)) + b = 0 + b = b$, but also $(a + (-b)) + b = a + ((-b) + b) = a + 0 = a$. Hence $a = b$.

(iii) The zero element 0 was given as an element with a special property to do with *addition*. In proving that $a0 = 0$ we see that it has a special *multiplicative* property, so we may expect to use the distributive law that connects addition and multiplication:

$a = a1 = a(0 + 1) = a0 + a1$ (by **8**) $= a0 + a$. Therefore $0 = a + (-a) = (a0 + a) + (-a) = a0 + (a + (-a)) = a0 + 0 = a0$, i.e. $a0 = 0$.

(iv) $ab + a(-b) = a(b + (-b)) = a0 = 0$ (by (iii)). So $a(-b)$ is the negative of ab, i.e. $a(-b) = -(ab)$. We can show that $(-a)b = -(ab)$ similarly.

(v) $(-a)(-b) = -(a(-b)) = -(-(ab))$ (using (iv) twice) $= ab$, by (i).

(vi) $a + (-1)a = 1a + (-1)a = (1 + (-1))a = 0a = a0 = 0$. So $(-1)a$ is the negative of a, i.e. $(-1)a = (-a)$.

(vii) If $ab = ac$, then $ab - ac = 0$. So $ab + (-ac) = 0$. Hence $ab + a(-c) = 0$, which gives $a(b + (-c)) = 0$. By **9**, either $a = 0$ or $b + (-c) = 0$. Thus either $a = 0$ or $b - c = 0$, i.e. $a = 0$ or $b = c$.

5. Further Examples of Integral Domains

Example 4. Let $J[\sqrt{2}]$ denote the set of all numbers $a + b\sqrt{2}$, where a and b are integers, with addition and multiplication defined in the normal way for real numbers. Then $J[\sqrt{2}]$ is an integral domain:

$J[\sqrt{2}]$ is closed under addition because the sum of two elements $a + b\sqrt{2}$ and $c + d\sqrt{2}$ is $(a + c) + (b + d)\sqrt{2}$, which is an element of $J[\sqrt{2}]$. The product of the two elements is $(ac + 2bd) + (bc + ad)\sqrt{2}$, so $J[\sqrt{2}]$ is closed under multiplication. The properties **1, 2, 5, 6, 8** hold for real numbers, so they hold for elements of $J[\sqrt{2}]$. The real numbers $0 = 0 + 0\sqrt{2}$, and $1 = 1 + 0\sqrt{2}$ both belong to $J[\sqrt{2}]$ and have the properties required in 3 and 7. If $a + b\sqrt{2}$ is an element of $J[\sqrt{2}]$, then so is $(-a) + (-b)\sqrt{2}$ which is its negative, so 4 holds. Finally, there can be no divisors of zero since we know that the product of two non-zero real numbers cannot be zero.

Actually, it is instructive to consider this example without assuming any properties of real numbers. First, notice that if $m + n\sqrt{2} = 0$, where m, n are integers, then $m = -n\sqrt{2}$, so $m^2 = 2n^2$. But the only integers satisfying this are $m = n = 0$ (see Theorem 24). So if the elements $a + b\sqrt{2}$ and $c + d\sqrt{2}$ are equal, then $(a - c) + (b - d)\sqrt{2} = 0$, and so $a = c$ and $b = d$. Thus each element of $J[\sqrt{2}]$ can be expressed uniquely in the form $a + b\sqrt{2}$. So we think of $a + b\sqrt{2}$ as simply a way of writing a pair of integers a, b in given order. We might write (a, b) instead. Addition and multiplication are defined by

$$(a, b) + (c, d) = (a + c, b + d)$$

and
$$(a, b)\, (c, d) = (ac + 2bd, bc + ad),$$

and the properties for an integral domain must be deduced from facts known about the integers. For example, to show that there are no divisors of zero, we suppose that $(a, b)\, (c, d) = (0, 0)$, the element on the right hand side obviously being the zero element. Then $(ac + 2bd, bc + ad) = (0, 0)$. We leave it as an exercise for the reader to show that the only solutions, in integers, to the equations $ac + 2bd = 0$ and $bc + ad = 0$ are either $a = b = 0$ or $c = d = 0$. So there are no divisors of zero.

Example 5. Let $\mathbf{R}[x]$ denote the set of all polynomials† in an indeterminate x, with real coefficients, with addition and multiplication defined in the normal way. Then $\mathbf{R}[x]$ is an integral domain:

If $f(x)$ is the polynomial $a_0 + a_1x + \ldots + a_nx^n$, and $g(x)$ is the polynomial $b_0 + b_1x + \ldots + b_mx^m$, we assume that the last coefficient is not equal to zero, unless the polynomial is the zero polynomial with all its coefficients zero. The sum of two polynomials is obtained by adding corresponding coefficients, and multiplication is given by

$$f(x)g(x) = a_0b_0 + (a_0b_1 + a_1b_0)x + (a_0b_2 + a_1b_1 + a_2b_0)x^2 \\ + \ldots + a_nb_mx^{m+n}.$$

Properties 1, 2, 5, 6, 8 for an integral domain can be established by using the fact that the coefficients satisfy the same laws. The zero polynomial is the zero element required by 3. The identity element is the identity polynomial, which has all its coefficients zero except the first term which is equal to the real number 1. The negative of $f(x)$ is the polynomial $(-a_0) + (-a_1)x + \ldots + (-a_n)x^n$, so 4 holds.

All that remains to be shown is that there are no divisors of zero: if $f(x)$ is not the zero polynomial, its last coefficient $a_n \neq 0$, and if $g(x)$ is not the

† A precise definition of a *polynomial* will be given in Chapter 6.

6

zero polynomial, $b_m \neq 0$. So the last coefficient $a_n b_m$ of the product is not zero, which shows that $f(x)g(x)$ is not the zero polynomial.

Example 6. Let $\mathbf{J_2}$ be the set consisting of two elements denoted by 0 and 1, with addition and multiplication given by the tables

+	0	1
0	0	1
1	1	0

×	0	1
0	0	0
1	0	1

Then $\mathbf{J_2}$ is an integral domain.

The tables are a convenient way of writing the information that $0 + 0 = 1 + 1 = 0, 0 + 1 = 1 + 0 = 1$ and $0.0 = 0.1 = 1.0 = 0, 1.1 = 1$. We can see by inspection that **2** and **6** hold. **1**, **5** and **8** can be established by considering, in each case, the eight possible combinations of values for a, b and c. The element which has already been denoted by 0 does indeed have the property **3**, and the other element which we have called 1 is the identity element required in **7**. Each element is its own negative, and finally **9** holds because the only non-zero element is 1 and $1.1 = 1 \neq 0$.

6. The Residue Classes

For each positive integer n, we may define a relation between integers as follows:

DEFINITION. *a is congruent to b modulo n if $a - b$ is a multiple of n. We write $a \equiv b$ (mod n).*

It is easy to see that a is congruent to b if and only if a and b have the same remainder when divided by n.

THEOREM 3. *The relation of congruence modulo n has the following properties:*

(i) *If a is any integer, $a \equiv a$ (mod n). This is called the* **reflexive** *property.*

(ii) *If a, b are any integers such that $a \equiv b$ (mod n), then $b \equiv a$ (mod n). This is called the* **symmetric** *property.*

(iii) *If a, b, c are any integers such that $a \equiv b$ (mod n) and $b \equiv c$ (mod n), then $a \equiv c$ (mod n). This is called the* **transitive** *property.*

Proof. (i) For any a, $a - a = 0$, which is a multiple of n, so $a \equiv a$ (mod n).

(ii) If $a \equiv b$ (mod n), then $a - b$ is a multiple of n. So $b - a$,

7

which is equal to $-(a - b)$, is also a multiple of n. Thus $b \equiv a$ (mod n).

(iii) If $a \equiv b$ (mod n) and $b \equiv c$ (mod n), then $a - b$ and $b - c$ are multiples of n. Then so also is $a - c$ for it is equal to the sum $(a - b) + (b - c)$. Hence $a \equiv c$ (mod n).

Any relation $\sim$ which is defined between two elements of a set, so that, for any a and b, the relation $a \sim b$ either does or does not hold, is called an **equivalence relation**† if it is reflexive, symmetric and transitive. It is an important fact that any equivalence relation divides up the set in question into a number of subsets called **equivalence classes** so that

every element is in one and only one of the classes,

if a and b are in the same class then $a \sim b$ holds, and if a and b are in different classes then $a \sim b$ does not hold.

In the case of congruence modulo n, with which we are at present concerned, the equivalence classes are called the **residue classes modulo** n. Two integers will be in the same class if they have the same remainder upon division by n. Thus the multiples of n form one class, the integers with remainder 1 another class, and so on. When the value of n is fixed and clearly understood, we can denote by $[a]$ the residue class modulo n containing a. Then there are n residue classes modulo n, and they can be called $[0], [1], [2], \ldots, [n - 1]$.

Example 7. The residue classes modulo 4 are

$[0] = \{\ldots, -8, -4, 0, 4, 8, 12, \ldots\}$,
$[1] = \{\ldots, -7, -3, 1, 5, 9, 13, \ldots\}$,
$[2] = \{\ldots, -6, -2, 2, 6, 10, 14, \ldots\}$,
$[3] = \{\ldots, -5, -1, 3, 7, 11, 15, \ldots\}$.

Notice that the class $[2]$ may equally well be called $[-6]$, for example, since a class is identified by any one of its elements.

We can now define how to add and multiply two residue

---

† Equivalence relations are treated more fully in *Sets and Groups*, by J. A. Green, in this Library.

classes: the sum and product of the class $[a]$ and the class $[b]$

are given by $$[a] + [b] = [a + b],$$

and $$[a] \cdot [b] = [ab].$$

We have to show that this is satisfactory by making sure that the sum and product are uniquely defined by these rules and that the result does not depend on which representatives a and b are chosen from the two classes. This is guaranteed by the following:

THEOREM 4. *If a and a' belong to the same residue class, and b and b' belong to the same residue class, then $a + b$ and $a' + b'$ belong to the same class, and ab and $a'b'$ belong to the same class.*

Proof. If $[a] = [a']$ and $[b] = [b']$, then $a = a' + kn$ and $b = b' + ln$, for some integers k, l. So $a + b = (a' + b') + (k + l)n$, which shows that $[a + b] = [a' + b']$; and secondly $ab = (a' + kn)(b' + ln) = a'b' + a'ln + b'kn + kln^2 = a'b' + (a'l + b'k + kln)n$, which shows that $[ab] = [a'b']$.

Example 8. Considering the residue classes modulo 4 (see Example 7), $[2]$ is the same class as $[-6]$, and $[3]$ is the same class as $[15]$. Then by definition $[2] + [3] = [5]$ and $[-6] + [15] = [9]$. But $[5]$ and $[9]$ are indeed the same class, normally denoted by $[1]$. So we may write $[2] + [3] = [1]$.

Similarly $[2][3] = [6]$ and $[-6][15] = [-90]$. But $6 - (-90) = 96$, which is a multiple of 4, so 6 and -90 belong to the same class, normally called $[2]$. So $[2][3] = [2]$.

THEOREM 5. *The set $\mathbf{J}_n$ of residue classes modulo n, with the addition and multiplication described, satisfy laws* **1** *to* **8** *(page 2).*

Proof. **1, 2, 5, 6, 8** can each be established for residue classes from the corresponding property of the integers. For example $[a]([b] + [c]) = [a][b + c] = [a(b + c)]$, and $[a][b] + [a][c] = [ab] + [ac] = [ab + ac]$. The distributive law holds for integers, so $a(b + c) = ab + ac$. Thus the distributive law holds for residue classes.

9

[0] is the zero element since $[a] + [0] = [a + 0] = [a]$, for any class $[a]$. $[-a]$ is the negative of $[a]$ since $[a] + [-a] = [a + (-a)] = [0]$. [1] is the identity element since $[a][1] = [a1] = [a]$, for any class $[a]$.

The elements of J_2 are strictly [0] and [1], but if there is no confusion these may be denoted by 0 and 1, and the addition and multiplication are then as given in Example 6. In the same way, we may denote the residue classes modulo 4, for example, by the symbols 0, 1, 2, 3 with addition and multiplication "modulo 4." Thus in J_4, $2 + 3 = 1$ and $2.3 = 2$ (see Example 8). The addition and multiplication can be displayed in tables; the tables for J_4, for instance, are

+	0	1	2	3
0	0	1	2	3
1	1	2	3	0
2	2	3	0	1
3	3	0	1	2

×	0	1	2	3
0	0	0	0	0
1	0	1	2	3
2	0	2	0	2
3	0	3	2	1

THEOREM 6. J_n *is an integral domain if and only if n is prime.*
Proof. Because of Theorem 5, all that needs to be shown is that there are no divisors of zero if and only if n is prime.

If n is not prime, then $n = n_1 n_2$, where n_1, n_2 are less than n and not zero. Then $[n_1][n_2] = [n] = [0]$. So $[n_1]$ and $[n_2]$ are divisors of zero.

Suppose n is prime, and suppose $[a][b] = [0]$. Then, since $[ab] = [0]$, ab is a multiple of n, i.e. n divides ab. Now, if n is prime, this implies that either n divides a or n divides b (see Theorem 21(i)). If n divides a, a is a multiple of n, so $[a] = [0]$, and if n divides b, then $[b] = [0]$. Thus there are no divisors of zero.

Excercises for this chapter will be found on p. 70.

CHAPTER TWO

Ordered and Well-Ordered Integral Domains

7. Order

The integers, of course, have properties that cannot be deduced from the basic postulates for an integral domain. Indeed, we have assumed some of them in the last section in order to give the residue classes modulo a prime as a further example of an integral domain. There is, for instance, the relation "$<$" between integers which has various properties. Thus we may distinguish the integers from some, but not all, of the other examples already mentioned, as being an ordered integral domain, that is, one in which such a relation exists. The definition can be given directly (see Exercise 4) or in terms of a notion of positiveness as follows:

DEFINITION. *An integral domain is* **ordered** *if certain elements may be called positive in such a way that*

P1. *the sum of any two positive elements is positive,*

P2. *the product of any two positive elements is positive,*

P3. *for any element a, one and only one of the following statements is true: a is positive, $a = 0$, $(-a)$ is positive* (**The Law of Trichotomy**).

Example 9. The idea of saying that certain integers, rational or real numbers are positive is familiar, and **P1, P2** and **P3** are satisfied. Thus **J**, **Q** and **R** are ordered integral domains.

Example 10. The elements of $J[\sqrt{2}]$ are real numbers, so those elements which as real numbers are positive may be called positive. Then **P1, P2** and **P3** hold for elements of $J[\sqrt{2}]$ because they hold for real numbers. So $J[\sqrt{2}]$ is an ordered integral domain.

ORDERED INTEGRAL DOMAINS

THEOREM 7. *In an ordered integral domain*
(i) *any non-zero element squared is positive,*
(ii) *the identity element is positive.*

Proof. (i) Suppose $a \neq 0$. Then, either a or $(-a)$ is positive, by **P3**. By definition, $a^2 = a.a$, so if a is positive, a^2 is positive by **P2**. On the other hand, if $(-a)$ is positive, then $(-a)(-a)$ is positive by **P2**, and, from Theorem 2(v), $(-a)(-a) = a.a = a^2$. Thus a^2 is again positive.

(ii) The identity element 1 is equal to $1.1 = 1^2$. So 1 is positive by (i).

Example 11. It is left as an exercise to show that in an ordered integral domain, any sum of a finite number of positive elements is positive. This being so, if J_n were ordered, [1] would be positive by Theorem 7(ii), and so the sum $[1] + \ldots + [1]$ (n times) would give a positive element. But in J_n this sum is equal to zero, which is not positive. This shows that J_n is not an ordered integral domain.

Example 12. The integral domain **C** of complex numbers is not ordered. Suppose it is. Then the element 1 is positive. Now consider the element i: either i or $-i$ is positive by **P3**. If i is positive, then i^2, which equals -1, is positive, contradicting **P3**. The alternative is that $(-i)$ is positive, but then $(-i)^2$, which also equals -1, is positive. Thus **C** is not ordered.

Having certain elements called positive, we can now explain what is meant by one element being less than another:

DEFINITION. *The relation* $<$ *is given by:* $a < b$ *if* $b - a$ *is positive.*

It is easy to see that the positive elements are then those elements b such that $0 < b$.

THEOREM 8. *The relation* $<$ *is transitive.*
Proof. Suppose that $a < b$ and $b < c$. Then, $b - a$ and $c - b$ are positive, so $c - a$, which equals $(b - a) + (c - b)$, is positive by **P1**. Thus $a < c$.

THEOREM 9. *The relation* $<$ *has the following properties:*
O1. *If* $a < b$, *then* $a + c < b + c$.

12

O2. *If $a < b$ and $0 < c$, then $ac < bc$.*

O3. *For any two elements a and b, one and only one of the following relations holds: $a < b$, $a = b$, $b < a$.*

Proof. **O1.** If $a < b$, then $b - a$ is positive. So $(b + c) - (a + c)$, which equals $b - a$, is positive. Thus $a + c < b + c$.

O2. If $a < b$ and $0 < c$, then $b - a$ and c are positive. So, $bc - ac$, being equal to $(b - a)c$, is positive by **P2**. Thus $ac < bc$.

O3. For any two elements a and b, consider $b - a$. By **P3**, one and only one of the following holds: $b - a$ is positive (in which case $a < b$), or $b - a = 0$ (in which case $a = b$), or $-(b - a)$ is positive (in which case $a - b$ is positive and $b < a$). Hence **O3** holds.

Clearly, there is other familiar terminology that we can use in an ordered integral domain. Thus we say $a > b$ if $b < a$, and we write $a \leq b$ as an abbreviation for "$a < b$ or $a = b$", and $a \geq b$ if $b \leq a$. We can also call certain elements negative and prove well-known properties:

DEFINITION. *In an ordered integral domain, a is **negative** if $(-a)$ is positive.*

THEOREM 10. *In an ordered integral domain*
 (i) *if a is positive, $(-a)$ is negative,*
 (ii) *a is negative if and only if $a < 0$,*
(iii) *the sum of two negative elements is negative,*
 (iv) *the product of two negative elements is positive,*
  (v) *the product of a negative element and a positive element is negative.*

The proof is left as an exercise.

DEFINITION. *If a is an element of an ordered integral domain, the **absolute value** of a, denoted by $|a|$, is a itself if $a \geq 0$ and $-a$ if $a < 0$.*

Thus $|a|$ is positive except when $a = 0$.

13

ORDERED INTEGRAL DOMAINS

THEOREM 11. (i) $|ab| = |a| \cdot |b|$, (ii) $|a + b| \leq |a| + |b|$.

Proof. (i) We consider the different possibilities: if a or b is zero, then the left hand side $|ab|$ and the right hand side $|a| \cdot |b|$ are both zero and so equal. If a and b are both positive, both sides equal ab. If a and b are both negative, the right hand side is equal to $(-a)(-b)$, and the left hand side equals ab, since ab is positive. The two sides are equal by Theorem 2(v). If a, say, is positive and b is negative, the right hand side equals $a(-b)$, and the left hand side is equal to $-(ab)$ since ab is negative. The two sides are equal by Theorem 2(iv).

(ii) Certainly $a \leq |a|$ and $b \leq |b|$, so $a + b \leq |a| + |b|$. Also, $-a \leq |a|$ and $-b \leq |b|$, so $-(a + b) = (-a) + (-b) \leq |a| + |b|$. But $|a + b|$ is either $a + b$ or $-(a + b)$, so $|a + b| \leq |a| + |b|$.

8. Well-Order

There is one final property which we can add to those already given for an ordered integral domain which will characterise the integers, so that we then have sufficient from which to deduce every other property of the integers:

DEFINITION. *An ordered integral domain is* **well-ordered** *if every non-empty subset S of the set of positive elements has a* **smallest** *element x such that $x \leq a$ for all a in S.*

We shall be able to show that the integers as we know them are essentially the only well-ordered integral domain. Or we may define the set of integers to be the one, essentially unique, well-ordered integral domain.

THEOREM 12. *In any well-ordered integral domain, there are no elements between 0 and 1.*

Proof. Suppose that there is an element between 0 and 1. Then the set S of all such is a non-empty set of positive elements, so let x be the smallest element in S. Then $0 < x < 1$ and thus $0 < x^2 < x$ (by **O2**) < 1. So x^2 is an element of S

14

which is smaller than x. This contradiction shows that there is no element between 0 and 1.

THEOREM 13. *A set S of elements of a well-ordered integral domain, which contains 1 and contains $a + 1$ whenever it contains a, contains all the positive elements of the domain.*

Proof. Let S' be the set of all positive elements not in S. If S' is not empty, let x be the smallest element in S'. Then $x - 1$ is not in S' but is positive, since $x > 1$, so $x - 1$ is in S. But then $(x - 1) + 1$, i.e. x itself, is in S. Since x is in S', i.e. not in S, we have a contradiction which shows that S' is empty and S contains all the positive elements.

If, in a well-ordered integral domain, we denote as usual the zero and identity elements by 0 and 1, and we denote $1 + 1$ by 2, $2 + 1$ by 3, $3 + 1$ by 4 and so on, Theorem 13 shows that in this way we get all the positive elements of the domain. Clearly 0 and the negatives of the positive elements are the only other elements. If the elements of two well-ordered domains are labelled in this way, then any property concerned with addition, multiplication and order involving the elements of one domain is also shared by the corresponding elements in the other domain. Thus we may define the set of integers as the one, essentially unique, well-ordered integral domain.†

Exercises for this chapter will be found on p. 70.

---

† We shall be able to make a more precise statement of what is meant here, later in the book (see Exercise 18, Chapter 5) when the notion of *isomorphism* has been introduced.

CHAPTER THREE

The Integers

---

9. The Principles of Induction

You may already have met in school algebra the principle of mathematical induction which is used in many branches of mathematics to prove a theorem which states that a certain result is true for all positive integers n. The procedure is first to prove the result for $n = 1$. Then, assuming the result for $n = k$ (say), we prove that it is true for $n = k + 1$. We conclude that it is therefore true for all positive integers. The justification for this is, loosely, that we know it is true for $n = 1$, so (with $k = 1$) it is true for $n = 2$. Now, with $k = 2$, we deduce that it is true for $n = 3$, and so on. But it is to avoid an "and so on" argument that the Principle of Induction is called into play. The essential point is that if we start with the integer 1, and successively add 1, then we do indeed get all the positive integers. This follows easily from Theorem 13, and we state it like this:

THEOREM 14 (**The First Principle of Induction**). *Let there be associated with each positive integer n, a proposition $P(n)$ which is either true or false. If $P(1)$ is true, and, for all k, $P(k)$ implies $P(k + 1)$, then $P(n)$ is true for all positive integers n.*

Proof. The set of those n for which $P(n)$ is true satisfies the conditions for S in Theorem 13; so it contains all the positive integers. Thus $P(n)$ is true for all n.

Sometimes it is easier to show that $P(k + 1)$ is true assuming that $P(n)$ is true for all values of n up to and including k, and not just for k alone. If we can do this for all k, then we may

DIVISIBILITY

again conclude that $P(n)$ is true for all positive integers by appealing to the Second Principle:

THEOREM 15 (**The Second Principle of Induction**). *Let there be associated with each positive integer n, a proposition P(n) which is either true or false. If P(1) is true, and P(k + 1) is true whenever P(1) ..., P(k) are true, then P(n) is true for all positive integers n.*

Proof. Let S be the set of positive integers for which $P(n)$ is true, and let S' be the set of positive integers not in S. If S' is not empty, let x be the smallest element in S'. Then $x > 1$, since 1 belongs to S, and 1, ..., $x - 1$ are in S. So $P(1)$, ..., $P(x - 1)$ are true, and hence $P(x)$ is true. But then x is in S, which is a contradiction. Therefore S' is empty and $P(n)$ is true for all positive integers n.

10. Divisibility

Many of the results of elementary number theory which are concerned with properties of the integers arise from the relation "*a* divides *b*" which exists between integers. However, this is no new relation for which we need to make postulates, as we did for "<". We can define the relation from the multiplicative structure that we already have, and we can establish all its familiar properties.

DEFINITION. *a* **divides** *b if there is an integer c such that ac = b. We write a | b. We say a is a* **divisor** *or* **factor** *of b, b is* **divisible** *by a and b is a* **multiple** *of a.*

Clearly, any integer divides itself (the relation is reflexive), any integer divides zero, and the only integer that zero divides is itself.

THEOREM 16.
(i) *If a | b and b | c, then a | c (the relation is transitive).*
(ii) *If a | b, then ac | bc.*
(iii) *If a | b and a | c, then a | (mb + nc), where m and n are any integers.*

17

THE INTEGERS

Proof. (i) If $a \mid b$ and $b \mid c$, there are integers d, e such that $ad = b$ and $be = c$. Then $ade = c$, so $a \mid c$.

(ii) If $a \mid b$, there is an integer d such that $ad = b$. Then $(ac)d = bc$, so $ac \mid bc$.

(iii) If $a \mid b$ and $a \mid c$, then $b = ad$ and $c = ae$ say. So $mb + nc = mad + nae = a(md + ne)$. Hence $a \mid (mb + nc)$.

THEOREM 17.
(i) *The only divisors of 1 are 1 and -1.*
(ii) *If $a \mid b$ and $b \mid a$, then $a = b$ or $a = -b$.*
(iii) *If $a \mid b$, where a and b are positive, then $a \leq b$.*

Proof. (i) Clearly 1 and -1 are divisors of 1. Suppose that $a \mid 1$; then for some c, $ac = 1$. Using the absolute value, $|a| \cdot |c| = |ac| = 1$. Neither $|a|$ or $|c|$ can be zero, so $|a| \geq 1$ and $|c| \geq 1$. But if $|a| > 1$, then $|a| \cdot |c| > |c|$, and so $|a| \cdot |c| > 1$. Therefore $|a| = 1$, i.e. $a = 1$ or -1.

(ii) If $a \mid b$ and $b \mid a$, then $ac = b$ and $bd = a$. Therefore $acd = a$ and so $cd = 1$. Thus d divides 1, so $d = \pm 1$. Hence $a = \pm b$.

(iii) If $a \mid b$, then $ac = b$, and if a and b are positive, then c is positive, i.e. $c \geq 1$. Therefore $ac \geq a$, i.e. $b \geq a$.

If an integer a is not divisible by the integer b, we are used to "dividing" a by b and getting a remainder. But there is no *operation* of division between integers. What is meant can be stated precisely however:

THEOREM 18 (**The Division Algorithm**). *For given integers a and b, with $b > 0$, there exist unique integers q and r such that $a = bq + r$, where $0 \leq r < b$.*

Proof. If, for some integer q, $a - bq = 0$, then $a = bq$ as required with $r = 0$. If not, let S be the set of all positive integers of the form $a - bk$, where k is an integer. Let r be the smallest element in S. Then $r = a - bq$ (say) and $r > 0$. Moreover, $r < b$, for if $r = b$ then $a = b(q + 1)$, and if $r > b$

See Back page. 18

then $a - b(q + 1)$ is an element of S smaller than r. Thus $a = bq + r$, with $0 < r < b$.

To show uniqueness, suppose that $a = bq_1 + r_1 = bq_2 + r_2$. We may suppose that $r_1 \geq r_2$. Then $r_1 - r_2 = b(q_2 - q_1)$. Thus $b \mid (r_1 - r_2)$, but $r_1 - r_2 < b$. From Theorem 17 (iii), we must have $r_1 - r_2 = 0$. Hence $r_1 = r_2$ and $q_1 = q_2$.

11. Highest Common Factor

We define now the highest common factor of two integers a and b, not simply as the largest number which is a factor of both (which might seem the obvious way), but as a common factor which is a multiple of any other common factor of the two integers.

DEFINITION. *An integer d is a* **highest common factor (h.c.f.)** *of a and b if $d \mid a$ and $d \mid b$, and if $x \mid a$ and $x \mid b$ imply that $x \mid d$. We write $d = (a, b)$.*

If we had defined the h.c.f. as the number d such that $d \mid a$ and $d \mid b$, and $x \mid a$ and $x \mid b$ imply $x \leq d$, we should have had to prove that the h.c.f. had the additional property of being a multiple of every other common factor. With the present approach, we need to prove that any two numbers do indeed have an h.c.f. with the properties of the definition. The advantage of the given definition is that it is all in terms of the one relation "$\mid$", which exists wherever there is multiplication, and this means that you can define an h.c.f. of two elements in a situation where there is no relation "$<$", as we shall see in § 28.

THEOREM 19. *Any two non-zero integers a and b have a unique positive highest common factor d, and there are integers s and t such that $d = sa + tb$.*

Proof. Let S be the set of all positive integers that can be expressed as $ha + kb$, for any integers h and k. S is not empty, so let d be the smallest element in S. Then $d = sa + tb$ say. We shall show that every element of S is a multiple of d:

19

If $ha + kb$ is an element of S, write $ha + kb = qd + r$, where $0 \leq r < b$, using the Division Algorithm. So $r = ha + kb - qd = ha + kb - q(sa + tb) = (h - qs)a + (k - qt)b$. If r were positive, it would be an element of S less than d. Thus $r = 0$, and $ha + kb$ is divisible by d.

If a is positive, then a belongs to S, since $a = 1a + 0b$, so $d \mid a$. If a is negative, it is $-a$ that belongs to S, but then $d \mid -a$ and hence $d \mid a$ also. Similarly $d \mid b$, and so this number d is a common factor of a and b. It is the highest common factor, for if $x \mid a$ and $x \mid b$, then $x \mid (sa + tb)$, by Theorem 16 (iii), i.e. $x \mid d$.

To show the uniqueness, suppose that d and d' are both h.c.fs of a and b. Certainly $d \mid a$ and $d \mid b$, so $d \mid d'$, because d' is an h.c.f. But also $d' \mid a$ and $d' \mid b$, so $d' \mid d$, because d is an h.c.f. By Theorem 17(ii), $d' = \pm d$. But both d and d' are positive so they must be equal, which proves the uniqueness.

A method, known as **Euclid's Algorithm,** is a practical way of finding the h.c.f. of two integers a, b. This relies on the fact that if we write $a = bq_1 + r_1$ (assuming that $a > b > 0$), then if $r_1 = 0$ the h.c.f. of a and b is b, and if $r_1 \neq 0$ the h.c.f. of a and b is the same as the h.c.f. of b and r_1, which are smaller numbers to deal with. The method can be repeated by writing $b = r_1 q_2 + r_2$, and then $(a, b) = (b, r_1) = (r_1, r_2)$. Continuing like this, you will eventually reach a zero remainder, and the last non-zero remainder is the h.c.f. of the original two numbers. The method also provides a way of finding integers s and t such that the h.c.f. $= sa + tb$, which is best seen by a numerical example:

Example 13. Let us use Euclid's Algorithm to find the h.c.f. of $a = 2145$ and $b = 1274$, and to express it as $sa + tb$.

We write $2145 = 1.1274 + 871$,

$$1274 = 1.871 + 403,$$
$$871 = 2.403 + 65,$$
$$403 = 6.65 + 13,$$
$$65 = 5.13.$$

So $(2145, 1274) = (1274, 871) = (871, 403) = (403, 65) = (65, 13) = 13$.

To express the h.c.f. as $sa + tb$, we use the above equations in turn to express each of the remainders in that form, until we reach the last remainder which is the h.c.f.

Thus
$$871 = 2145 - 1.1274 = a - b,$$
$$403 = 1274 - 1.871 = b - 1(a - b) = -a + 2b,$$
$$65 = 871 - 2.403 = (a - b) - 2(-a + 2b) = 3a - 5b,$$
$$13 = 403 - 6.65 = (-a + 2b) - 6(3a - 5b) = -19a + 32b,$$

as required.

12. Primes

DEFINITION. *A positive integer p is* **prime** *if $p \neq 1$, and if the only divisors of p are ± 1 and $\pm p$. Otherwise the integer is* **composite.**

DEFINITION. *If $(a, b) = 1$, a and b are* **relatively prime.**

THEOREM 20. *If $(a, b) = 1$, and $a \mid bc$, then $a \mid c$.*

Proof. Since $(a, b) = 1$, there are integers s and t such that $1 = sa + tb$. Therefore $c = sac + tbc$. But $a \mid bc$, so divides both terms on the right hand side. Hence $a \mid c$.

THEOREM 21. *If p is prime,*
(i) *$p \mid ab$ implies $p \mid a$ or $p \mid b$,*
(ii) *$p \mid a_1 a_2 \ldots a_n$ implies $p \mid a_i$ for some i.*

Proof. (i) Suppose that $p \mid ab$, but p does not divide a. The only positive factors of p are 1 and p, and p does not divide a, so 1 is the h.c.f. of p and a, i.e. $(p, a) = 1$. By Theorem 20, $p \mid b$ as required.

(ii) Let $P(n)$ be the statement "If p is prime then for any n integers $a_1, \ldots, a_n$, $p \mid a_1 a_2 \ldots a_n$ implies $p \mid a_i$ for some i, where $1 \leq i \leq n$." Certainly $P(1)$ is true. Suppose that $a_1, \ldots, a_{k+1}$ are any $k + 1$ integers. If $p \mid a_1 a_2 \ldots a_{k+1}$, then, if we put $b = a_1 a_2 \ldots a_k$, $p \mid b a_{k+1}$. From (i), we may deduce that either $p \mid b$ or $p \mid a_{k+1}$. Assuming now that $P(k)$ is true, we have either $p \mid a_i$ for some i where $1 \leq i \leq k$, or $p \mid a_{k+1}$. Thus we have proved $P(k + 1)$. By the First Principle of Induction, $P(n)$ is true for all positive integers n.

THE INTEGERS

13. Unique Factorisation

We are now in a position to prove that any integer can be factorised into primes, and that this can be done in only one way.

THEOREM 22 (**The Fundamental Theorem of Arithmetic**). *Any integer except zero can be expressed as* $+1$ *or* -1 *times a product of primes. This expression is unique except for the order in which the primes occur.*

Proof. First we prove that any positive integer can be factorised into a product of primes. Let $P(a)$ be the proposition "a can be factorised into $+1$ times a product of primes." $P(1)$ is true since 1 is $+1$ times a product of no primes. Suppose that $a > 1$. If a is prime, then $P(a)$ is true, since a is $+1$ times a product consisting of the single prime a. If a is not prime, then $a = bc$ where $b < a$ and $c < a$. Assuming that $P(k)$ is true for all $k < a$, we can write b as a product of a set of primes and we can write c as a product of a set of primes. Then a is the product of the two sets of primes. Thus $P(a)$ is true. By the Second Principle of Induction, we can assert that $P(a)$ is true for all positive integers a.

To prove the uniqueness of this factorisation, suppose that $p_1 p_2 \ldots p_r = q_1 q_2 \ldots q_s$, where $p_1, \ldots, p_r, q_1, \ldots, q_s$ are prime. Then $p_1 \mid q_1 q_2 \ldots q_s$, so $p_1 \mid q_i$, for some i. Since q_i is prime and $p_1 \neq 1$ and both are positive, $p_1 = q_i$. We may now cancel p_1 and q_i, and continue similarly with p_2. In this way, we can show that $r = s$, and that $q_1, \ldots, q_s$ are just $p_1, \ldots, p_r$ in possibly a different order.

If a is negative, then a can be expressed uniquely as -1 times the unique factorisation of the positive integer $-a$.

Finally, we have two theorems amongst the most famous in mathematics which, with their proofs, are remarkable for their simplicity and elegance:

22

UNIQUE FACTORISATION

THEOREM 23 (*due to Euclid*). *There are infinitely many primes.*

Proof. If $p_1, ..., p_n$ are prime, then $N = p_1 p_2 ... p_n + 1$ is a number which is not divisible by any of these primes. For $p_i \mid N$ implies that $p_i \mid 1$. So the number N has prime factors, by Theorem 22, which are not in the list $p_1, ..., p_n$. Therefore, for any finite set of primes, there is another prime not in the set.

THEOREM 24 (*due to Pythagoras*). $\sqrt{2}$ *is irrational.*

Proof. Suppose that $\sqrt{2} = m/n$ where m and n are integers. If m and n have any common factor, this may be cancelled until $\sqrt{2} = a/b$, where a and b have h.c.f. 1. Then $a = b\sqrt{2}$, so $a^2 = 2b^2$. Thus $2 \mid a^2$, from which we deduce that $2 \mid a$, by Theorem 21(i). Let $a = 2c$, where c is an integer. Then $4c^2 = 2b^2$, i.e. $2c^2 = b^2$. Thus $2 \mid b^2$ which implies that $2 \mid b$. Hence 2 is a common factor of a and b, which is a contradiction. This proves that $\sqrt{2}$ is irrational.

Exercises for this chapter will be found on p. 71.

CHAPTER FOUR

Fields

---

14. Definition of a Field

We are now going to study integral domains in which division is possible. Examples will be the set **Q** of rational numbers and the set **R** of real numbers, in which you can divide by any element (except zero). We shall develop division from the existence of inverses:

DEFINITION. *A set F is a **field** if F is closed under two operations, addition and multiplication, satisfying properties **1** to **8** (see p. 2) and*

10. *For each $a \neq 0$, there is an element, denoted by a^{-1}, called the **inverse** of a, such that $a^{-1}a = 1$.*

Any field is certainly an integral domain, because there can be no divisors of zero in a field: Suppose that $ab = 0$. If $a \neq 0$, a has an inverse a^{-1} and then $a^{-1}(ab) = a^{-1}0 = 0$. So $(a^{-1}a)b = 0$, i.e. $b = 0$. So either $a = 0$ or $b = 0$, which shows that property **9** holds.

We leave it as an exercise to show that each non-zero element has a *unique* inverse. We may then show that the equation $ax = b$, where $a \neq 0$, always has a unique solution, for multiplication, on the left, by a^{-1} gives $x = a^{-1}b$, which is therefore the required solution. Since $a^{-1}b$ is equal to ba^{-1}, by **6**, either of these may be denoted by b/a. So, if we wish, a^{-1} itself can be written as $1/a$.

15. Examples of Fields

Example 14. **Q** is a field; for any non-zero rational number is m/n where $m \neq 0$, and then the rational number n/m is its inverse.

24

EXAMPLES OF FIELDS

Example 15. We shall assume that it is obvious that if a is a non-zero real number, there is a real number $1/a$ which is its inverse. Thus $\mathbf{R}$ is a field.

Example 16. The set $\mathbf{C}$ of complex numbers is a field: If $a + bi$ is a non-zero complex number, then a and b are not both zero, and you can verify by multiplication that the number $a/(a^2 + b^2) + (-b)i/(a^2 + b^2)$ is its inverse.

Example 17. The set of integers is not a field. The only elements that have inverses are ± 1. For instance, 2 does not have an inverse because there is no integer a such that $2a = 1$. Alternatively, we may say that multiplication between integers is the same as multiplication between them considered as real numbers. Then the inverse of 2 is $\frac{1}{2}$ which is not an integer.

Example 18. $\mathbf{J}[\sqrt{2}]$ is not a field (see Example 4). Multiplication between the elements is the same as multiplication between them considered as real numbers. You can verify by multiplication that the inverse of $a + b\sqrt{2}$ is $a/(a^2 - 2b^2) + (-b)\sqrt{2}/(a^2 - 2b^2)$. There are clearly cases when $a/(a^2 - 2b^2)$ and $(-b)/(a^2 - 2b^2)$ are not integers, so the inverse does not belong to $\mathbf{J}[\sqrt{2}]$. For instance, we may again take 2, which is an element of $\mathbf{J}[\sqrt{2}]$, but its inverse $\frac{1}{2}$ is not.

Example 19. $\mathbf{R}[x]$ is not a field (see Example 5). In fact, the non-zero scalars are the only elements that have inverses. For instance, the polynomial $x + 1$ has no inverse as there is no polynomial $f(x)$ such that $(x + 1) f(x) = 1$. The left hand side has degree $\geqslant 1$ and so cannot equal the right hand side which has degree 0.

Example 20. The set $\mathbf{J}_p$ of residue classes modulo p (prime) is a field. We know that $\mathbf{J}_p$ is an integral domain (Theorem 6), so we need to prove **10**: For any residue class $[a] \neq 0$, we must find a class $[x]$ such that $[a] [x] = [1]$. Since p is prime, and p does not divide a, the h.c.f. of a and p is 1. Hence $1 = xa + yp$, for some integers x and y, by Theorem 19. With this x, $[a] [x] = [ax] = [1 - yp] = [1]$, since $1 - yp$ and 1 differ by a multiple of p. So every non-zero residue class modulo p has an inverse.

In fact, there is an alternative way of proving that $\mathbf{J}_p$ is a field; it follows immediately from the more general theorem:

THEOREM 25. *Any integral domain with a finite number of elements is a field.*

Proof. Let a_0, a_1, a_2, ..., a_n be the distinct elements of the integral domain, with $a_0 = 0$ and $a_1 = 1$. If $i \neq 0$, then $a_i a_1$, $a_i a_2$, ..., $a_i a_n$ are all non-zero and all different, since $a_i a_h = a_i a_k$ implies $a_h = a_k$, by Theorem 2(vii). Thus $a_i a_1$, ..., $a_i a_n$ are just a_1, ..., a_n in possibly a different order. So, for some j,

25

$a_i a_j = a_1 = 1$. Hence a_j is the inverse of a_i and every non-zero element has an inverse.

16. Subfields

DEFINITION. *A subset S of a field F which is a field with the same addition and multiplication as F is a* **subfield** *of F. If $S \neq F$, S is a* **proper** *subfield.*

THEOREM 26. *A subset S of a field F is a subfield if*
(i) *S is closed under addition and multiplication,*
(ii) *S contains the 0 and 1 of F,*
(iii) *for each a in S, $(-a)$ is in S, and for each $a \neq 0$ in S, a^{-1} is in S.*

Proof. The properties **1, 2, 5, 6, 8** hold for addition and multiplication between the elements of S, because they hold between any elements of F, as F is a field. Moreover, (ii) ensures that **3** and **7** hold, while (iii) ensures that **4** and **10** hold. So S is a subfield.

THEOREM 27. *If S_1 and S_2 are subfields of a field F, then the intersection $S_1 \cap S_2$ is a subfield of F.*

Proof. The intersection of two sets is defined in Example 2. If a, b are in $S_1 \cap S_2$, then a, b are both in S_1 and, since S_1 is a subfield, $a + b$ is also in S_1. Similarly $a + b$ is in S_2 and hence in the intersection. Thus $S_1 \cap S_2$ is closed under addition, and similarly under multiplication. Moreover, the 0 and 1 of F are both in S_1 and also in S_2 and hence in the intersection. Finally, if a is in $S_1 \cap S_2$, then a, and so $(-a)$, is in S_1. Also a, and so $(-a)$, is in S_2. Therefore $(-a)$ is in $S_1 \cap S_2$, and you can show similarly that the inverse of any non-zero element of the intersection is also in the intersection. $S_1 \cap S_2$ is a subfield by Theorem 26.

Example 21. **Q** and **R** are subfields of **C**. **Q** is a subfield of **R**.

Example 22. Let **Q**$(\sqrt{2})$ denote the set of all real numbers of the form $a + b\sqrt{2}$, where a, b are *rational*. Referring to Example 4, the reader should

26

THE CHARACTERISTIC OF A FIELD

notice the similarity between $Q(\sqrt{2})$ and $J[\sqrt{2}]$ and should have no difficulty in showing that $Q(\sqrt{2})$ is closed under addition and multiplication, contains 0 and 1, and contains the negative of each of its elements. But, unlike $J[\sqrt{2}]$ (see Example 18), $Q(\sqrt{2})$ contains also the inverse of each of its non-zero elements. For the inverse of $a + b\sqrt{2}$ is $c + d\sqrt{2}$, where $c = a/(a^2 - 2b^2)$ and $d = (-b)/(a^2 - 2b^2)$. Here c and d are rational, since a, b are rational, and, from the irrationality of $\sqrt{2}$, we can show that the denominator $a^2 - 2b^2$ is only zero when $a = b = 0$. Thus $Q(\sqrt{2})$ is a subfield of R.

17. The Characteristic of a Field

The examples of fields that we have seen so far have been of two distinct kinds: there are the subfields of the complex numbers, which are called **number fields**, such as Q, $Q(\sqrt{2})$, R and C itself, and there are the residue class fields J_p. One obvious difference between the two is that the first are all infinite, and the others are finite. There is a further difference in that a finite sum $1 + 1 + \ldots + 1$ is never equal to zero in the number fields, but must sometimes equal zero in the residue class fields. We shall find that a finite sum $1 + 1 + \ldots + 1$ may equal zero even in an infinite field (see Example 26), and so we characterise fields according to this property:

DEFINITION. *If, in a field F, $1 + 1 + \ldots + 1$ (m times) $= 0$, and if m is the smallest positive integer for which this is so, F has **characteristic** m. Otherwise F has **characteristic zero**.*

Example 23. The field J_p has characteristic p.

Example 24. Any subfield of the field C of complex numbers has characteristic zero.

THEOREM 28. *In a field of characteristic m, $a + a + \ldots + a$ (m times) $= 0$, for any element a.*

Proof. Using the distributive law, the sum of m terms $a + a + \ldots + a = a(1 + 1 + \ldots + 1) = a0 = 0$.

THEOREM 29. *A finite field cannot have characteristic zero.*

Proof. The elements $0, 1, 1 + 1, 1 + 1 + 1, \ldots$ in a finite field F cannot be all different, so eventually $1 + 1 + \ldots + 1$

27

(r times) $= 1 + 1 + \ldots + 1$ (s times), say, where $s < r$. Then $1 + 1 + \ldots + 1$ ($r - s$ times) $= 0$, so F has some non-zero characteristic $m \leq r - s$.

THEOREM 30. *The characteristic of a field is either zero or prime.*

Proof. Suppose that F has non-zero characteristic m. If $m = hk$, where $h < m$ and $k < m$, then

$$(\underbrace{1 + 1 + \ldots + 1}_{h \text{ times}})(\underbrace{1 + 1 + \ldots + 1}_{k \text{ times}}) = \underbrace{1 + 1 + \ldots + 1}_{m \text{ times}} = 0.$$

Therefore, either $1 + 1 + \ldots + 1$ (h times) $= 0$ or alternatively $1 + 1 + \ldots + 1$ (k times) $= 0$, because in a field there are no divisors of zero. This contradicts m being the smallest such integer. So m is prime.

Example 25. The four elements $0, 1, a, b$ with addition and multiplication tables as follows

+	0	1	a	b
0	0	1	a	b
1	1	0	b	a
a	a	b	0	1
b	b	a	1	0

×	0	1	a	b
0	0	0	0	0
1	0	1	a	b
a	0	a	b	1
b	0	b	1	a

form a field. The characteristic is 2, which is the only prime that divides 4 (see Exercise 11), and the elements 0 and 1 have addition and multiplication just like J_2.

Example 26. If F is any field, the set of all polynomials with coefficients in F form an integral domain, denoted by $F[x]$ (see § 25). A **rational function** over F is an expression $f(x)/g(x)$, where $f(x)$, $g(x)$ are polynomials with coefficients in F, with $g(x)$ not the zero polynomial, and the set of all rational functions over F form a field denoted by $F(x)$. If F has characteristic p, then $F(x)$ is an example of an infinite field with finite characteristic.

Exercises for this chapter will be found on p. 72.

CHAPTER FIVE

Rings

---

18. Definition of a Ring

We turn now to an algebraic structure which is more general than an integral domain, by discarding some of the postulates that we require to be satisfied. We shall keep to the numbering that we have been using so far.

DEFINITION. A **ring** *is a set R with two operations called addition and multiplication, denoted in the usual way, satisfying:*

1. *For all a, b, c in R, $a + (b + c) = (a + b) + c$,*

2. *For all a, b in R, $a + b = b + a$,*

3. *There is an element 0 in R such that $a + 0 = a$ for all a in R,*

4. *For each a in R, there is an element $(-a)$ such that $a + (-a) = 0$,*

5. *For all a, b, c in R, $a(bc) = (ab)c$,*

8. *For all a, b, c in R, $a(b + c) = ab + ac$,*
         and $(a + b)c = ac + bc$.

What we no longer ask is that there should be no divisors of zero, that there should be an identity element, and that multiplication should be commutative. If **6** does hold, R is called a **commutative ring,** and if **7** holds also, R is a **commutative ring with identity.**

Any integral domain is a ring, but the concept of a ring is more general than integral domain, which in turn is more general than field, because we require fewer postulates to hold. So we cannot assume that results proved for integral domains necessarily hold in rings. But we can show that, in a ring, the zero is unique, each element has a unique negative, and the rules given in Theorem 2(i) to (v) are valid. The following are examples of rings which are *not* integral domains.

Example 27. The set of all 2×2 real matrices form a ring, (see Example 3). This is not an integral domain because multiplication is not commutative.

Example 28. The set of even integers is a commutative ring. This is not an integral domain because there is no identity element.

Example 29. J_n, where n is composite, is a commutative ring with identity. This is not an integral domain because there are divisors of zero (see Theorems 5 and 6).

19. Subrings

DEFINITION. *A subset S of a ring R which is a ring with the same addition and multiplication as R is a* **subring** *of R.*

THEOREM 31. *A subset S of a ring R is a subring if*
(i) *S is closed under addition and multiplication,*
(ii) *S contains the 0 of R,*
(iii) *for each a in S, $(-a)$ is in S.*

The proof, which is similar to that of Theorem 26, is left to the reader.

THEOREM 32. *A non-empty subset of a ring R is a subring if, for all a and b in S, $a - b$ and ab are in S.*

Proof. If S satisfies the given conditions, then it contains an element a and hence the element $a - a = 0$. Then it contains also $0 - a = (-a)$. Given a and b in S, then ab is in S and, since $(-b)$ is in S, so is $a - (-b) = a + b$. Hence (i), (ii), (iii) of Theorem 31 are satisfied.

Example 30. The zero element alone forms a subring $\{0\}$ of any ring R. A subring of R which is neither $\{0\}$ nor R itself is a **proper** subring.

Example 31. The set of even integers is a subring of J.

Example 32. More generally, if n is any integer, the multiples of n form a subring of J.

Example 33. The set $J[i]$ of those complex numbers of the form $a + bi$, where a and b are integers is a subring of the ring C of all complex numbers. The elements of $J[i]$ are called **Gaussian integers**.

20. Cosets

We can now generalise what we did in §6, where the equivalence relation of congruence modulo n led from the ring of integers to the ring $\mathbf{J}_n$ of residue classes.

DEFINITION. *If S if a subring of a ring R, then, if a and b belong to R, a* **is congruent to** *b* **modulo** *S if $a - b$ belongs to S. We write $a \equiv b$ (mod S).*

THEOREM 33. *The relation of congruence modulo S is an equivalence relation.*

Proof. (i) If a is any element, then $a \equiv a$ (mod S) because $a - a = 0$ belongs to S.

(ii) Suppose that $a \equiv b$ (mod S), then $a - b$ belongs to S and hence so does its negative $-(a - b) = b - a$. Thus $b \equiv a$ (mod S).

(iii) Suppose $a \equiv b$ (mod S) and $b \equiv c$ (mod S). Then $a - b$ and $b - c$ are in S, and hence so is their sum $(a - b) + (b - c) = a - c$. Thus $a \equiv c$ (mod S).

Corresponding to this relation then, we shall get equivalence classes which are called the **cosets** of S. Let $[a]$ denote the coset containing the element a. S itself is actually one of the cosets, the coset $[0]$. $[a]$ consists of all elements $a + s$ with s in S, so an alternative notation for $[a]$ is $a + S$. If, in the ring of integers, S is the subring of all multiples of n, then the cosets of S are none other than the residue classes modulo n.

We now want to define addition and multiplication between the cosets in the way we did for residue classes. Unfortunately, we find that the natural definition for multiplication $[a] \cdot [b] = [ab]$, does not give an unambiguous result for the product unless the subring in question has a special property. Such subrings will be given the name *ideals* and these we must study before we proceed (in § 22) with the addition and multiplication of cosets.

31

RINGS

21. Ideals

DEFINITION. *A subring U of a ring R is an* **ideal** *if for all u in U, ru and ur also belong to U, for all r in R.*

Combining this definition with Theorem 32, we obtain the following set of sufficient conditions for a subset to be an ideal:

THEOREM 34. *A non-empty subset U of a ring R is an ideal if, for all u and v in U, u − v is in U and if ru and ur are in U, for all r in R.*

Example 34. In **J**, the set of all multiples of any integer a is an ideal.

Example 35. If a, b are any two integers, the set of all integers of the form $ha + kb$, for any integers h and k, is an ideal of **J**.

Example 36. In $\mathbf{J}_{12}$, the following sets are ideals: {0, 2, 4, 6, 8, 10}, {0, 3, 6, 9}, {0, 4, 8}, {0, 6}.

THEOREM 35. *If R is a ring with an identity element and U is an ideal containing the identity, then U = R.*

Proof. If U contains 1, then U also contains all multiples $r1$, with r in R, and so U is the whole ring R.

THEOREM 36. *A field has no proper ideals.*

Proof. If an ideal U of a field F contains a non-zero element a, then it also contains all multiples of a, in particular $a^{-1}a$ which equals 1. By the previous theorem, $U = F$.

In a commutative ring R with identity, we can see that, for any element a, the multiples ra, with r in R, form an ideal which contains a:

DEFINITION. *In a commutative ring R with identity, the ideal of all multiples ra, with r in R, is the* **principal ideal generated by** *a, and is denoted by* (a).

This important example of an ideal enables us to prove the converse of Theorem 36:

THEOREM 37. *A commutative ring with identity with no proper ideals is a field.*

32

Proof. If a is any non-zero element of R, the principal ideal (a), since it is not proper, is the whole of R. So the identity belongs to (a), i.e. for some r in R, $ra = 1$. Hence this element r is the inverse of a, and we have found that every non-zero element has an inverse.

THEOREM 38. *In* **J**, *every ideal is a principal ideal.*

Proof. If U is an ideal of **J**, let d be the smallest positive integer in U. We shall show that U is the principal ideal generated by d. If a is any element of U, write $a = qd + r$, where $0 \leq r < d$, using the Division Algorithm. Both a and qd are in U, and so r is in U. Then $r = 0$ for otherwise r would be a positive element of U smaller than d. Thus, a is divisible by d, and we have shown that every element of U is a multiple of d.

Clearly, the first part of the proof of Theorem 19 is the special case applying this theorem to the ideal given in Example 35.

THEOREM 39. *The intersection of two ideals of a ring R is an ideal of R.*

The proof is left as an exercise.

Example 37. In the ring of integers, for any two integers a and b, take the intersection of the two ideals (a) and (b). By Theorem 38, $(a) \cap (b)$ is a principal ideal (k), say. The integer k is the *least common multiple* of a and b (see Exercise 13, Chapter 3).

THEOREM 40. *If U, V are two ideals of a ring R, then the set of all elements $u + v$, with u in U and v in V, is an ideal of R. Let $U + V$ denote this ideal. Then $U \subseteq U + V$ and $V \subseteq U + V$.*

The proof is left as an exercise.

Example 38. In the ring of integers, the sum $(a) + (b)$ of two principal ideals consists of all integers of the form $ha + kb$, where h, k are integers. This is a principal ideal (d), where d is the *h.c.f.* of a and b (see Theorem 19).

22. Quotient Rings

We can now continue with our intention of defining the sum and product of two cosets, assuming now that we are taking cosets of an ideal U. Addition and multiplication are defined by

$$[a] + [b] = [a + b],$$
$$[a] \cdot [b] = [ab].$$

We need to show that the result of the sum and product are independent of the particular representatives a and b chosen:

THEOREM 41. *Suppose that U is an ideal of R, and that a, a' belong to the same coset of U, and b, b' belong to the same coset of U. Then $a + b$ and $a' + b'$ belong to the same coset, and ab and $a'b'$ belong to the same coset.*

Proof. If a, a' belong to the same coset, $a - a'$ is in U, so $a = a' + u_1$, with u_1 in U. Similarly, $b = b' + u_2$, with u_2 in U. Thus $a + b = (a' + b') + (u_1 + u_2)$ and so $(a + b) - (a' + b')$ is in U as required. Also, $ab = (a' + u_1)(b' + u_2) = a'b' + u_1b' + a'u_2 + u_1u_2$. Since U is an ideal, u_1b' and $a'u_2$ as well as u_1u_2 are in U, so $ab - a'b'$ is in U, as required.

THEOREM 42. *If U is an ideal of the ring R, then with the addition and multiplication described, the cosets of U form a ring. This is called a* **quotient ring** *of R and is denoted by R/U.*

Proof. **1, 2, 5, 8** can each be established for cosets from the corresponding property of the elements of R. Clearly, [0] is the zero element and $[-a]$ is the negative of $[a]$, so **3** and **4** hold. The reader will be able to fill in the details by referring if necessary to the proof of Theorem 5.

Example 39. If, in the ring $\mathbf{J}$ of integers, we take the principal ideal (n), the quotient ring $\mathbf{J}/(n)$ is the ring $\mathbf{J}_n$ of residue classes modulo n.

Example 40. In a ring R, R itself is an ideal and the quotient ring R/R is a ring consisting of a single zero element. The set $\{0\}$ is also an ideal of R and the quotient ring $R/\{0\}$ consists of cosets each containing a single element with addition and multiplication identical to R.

23. Maximal Ideals

The example $\mathbf{J}_p$ shows that it is possible for the quotient ring R/U to be a field, even when R is not; in the case of the ring of integers, the condition that a quotient ring be a field is that the ideal is the principal ideal generated by a prime. In general if R is a commutative ring with identity, we find that the necessary and sufficient condition that the quotient ring R/U is a field is that U is *maximal*:

DEFINITION. *The ideal U of a ring R is* **maximal** *if $U \neq R$ and there is no ideal V such that $U \subset V \subset R$.*

Example 41. In **J**, the principal ideal (n) is maximal if and only if n is prime: For, suppose n is prime and V is an ideal such that $(n) \subseteq V \subseteq \mathbf{J}$. Then $V = (h)$, say. $(n) \subseteq (h)$ implies that n is in (h), so $n = hk$, for some k. Since n is prime, either $h = \pm 1$, in which case $V = \mathbf{J}$, or $h = \pm n$, in which case $V = (n)$. Thus there is no ideal V such that $(n) \subset V \subset \mathbf{J}$, so (n) is maximal.

Conversely, if n is composite, $n = hk$, say, where $1 < h < n$. The ideal (h) satisfies $(n) \subset (h) \subset \mathbf{J}$, so (n) is not maximal.

THEOREM 43. *If R is a commutative ring with identity, the quotient ring R/U is a field if and only if U is maximal.*

Proof. Suppose that U is maximal. Let $[a]$ be a non-zero element of R/U. Since $[a] \neq [0]$, a is not an element of U. Form the ideal $V = U + (a)$, which consists of all elements $u + ra$, with u in U and r in R. Since U is maximal and $U \subset V$, V is the whole of R and so contains the identity element. In other words, for some u in U and r in R, $u + ra = 1$. With this r, $[r][a] = [1 - u] = [1]$, and $[r]$ is the inverse of $[a]$. So every non-zero element has an inverse and R/U is a field.

Conversely, if R/U is a field, let V be an ideal such that $U \subset V \subseteq R$. Take an element a of V which is not in U. Then $U + (a) \subset V$. But, since a is not in U, $[a]$ is a non-zero element of R/U and so has an inverse $[r]$ such that $[r][a] = [1]$. Then $ra - 1$ is in U, i.e. for some r in R and u in U, $ra - 1 = u$. So, $u + ra = 1$ and, by Theorem 35, this implies that $U + (a) = R$. Hence $V = R$ and so U is maximal.

24. Homomorphisms

We now introduce a way of comparing two rings R and R'. This will enable us to say in a precise way when two rings are rather alike, or when R and R' are essentially the same ring. The basic idea is to link each element of R with an element of R' so that the corresponding elements add and multiply in the same way:

DEFINITION. *A* **homomorphism** *of R into R' is a mapping ϕ, which determines for each element a of R an element denoted by $\phi(a)$ in R', which satisfies the conditions*
H1. $\phi(a + b) = \phi(a) + \phi(b)$,
H2. $\phi(ab) = \phi(a) \cdot \phi(b)$.

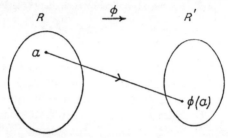

FIG. 1

In the equations **H1**, **H2**, the addition and multiplication that appear on the left hand side are those of the ring R, since a and b are in R; on the right hand side, the elements $\phi(a)$ and $\phi(b)$ are in R', so the addition and multiplication are those of R'. We write $\phi: R \to R'$, when ϕ is a mapping of R into R', the element $\phi(a)$ is called the **image** of a, and we say that a **is mapped onto** the element $\phi(a)$. Notice that not every element of R' is necessarily the image of an element of R, and it may happen that two elements of R have the same image.

THEOREM 44. *If $\phi : R \to R'$ is a homomorphism,*
(i) $\phi(0) = 0$, *(ϕ maps the zero element of R onto the zero element of R'),*
(ii) $\phi(-a) = -\phi(a)$, *for all a in R, (ϕ maps the negative of a onto the negative of $\phi(a)$),*
(iii) $\phi(a - b) = \phi(a) - \phi(b)$.

36

Proof. (i) $\phi(0) + \phi(0) = \phi(0 + 0)$ (by **H1**) $= \phi(0)$. So $\phi(0) = 0$, by subtracting $\phi(0)$ from both sides.

(ii) $\phi(a) + \phi(-a) = \phi(a + (-a))$ (by **H1**) $= \phi(0) = 0$. So $\phi(-a)$ is the negative of $\phi(a)$.

(iii) $\phi(a - b) = \phi(a + (-b)) = \phi(a) + \phi(-b)$ (by **H1**) $= \phi(a) + (-\phi(b)) = \phi(a) - \phi(b)$.

DEFINITION. *The set of those elements in R' which are images of elements of R is called the* **image** *of the homomorphism ϕ*:
$$\text{Im } \phi = \{x \mid \phi(a) = x, \text{for some } a \text{ in } R\}.$$

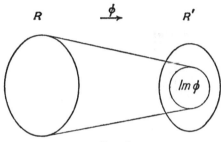

FIG. 2

DEFINITION. *The set of elements in R which are mapped onto the zero element of R' is called the* **kernel** *of the homomorphism ϕ*:
$$\text{Ker } \phi = \{a \mid \phi(a) = 0\}.$$

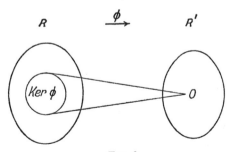

FIG. 3

37

THEOREM 45. *If Ker $\phi = \{0\}$, each element of Im ϕ is the image of just one element of R.*

Proof. If x is the image of a and b, then $\phi(a) = \phi(b) = x$. Hence $\phi(a) - \phi(b) = 0$, i.e. $\phi(a - b) = 0$. Thus $a - b$ belongs to the kernel of ϕ, which means in this case that $a - b = 0$, i.e. $a = b$. Thus x is the image of just one element.

If Ker $\phi = \{0\}$, ϕ is given the special name of **monomorphism**; if a homomorphism has Im ϕ equal to the whole of R', then ϕ is called an **epimorphism**. If ϕ is both an epimorphism and a monomorphism, ϕ is called an **isomorphism**. Thus ϕ is an isomorphism if, for every element x of R', there is a unique element a in R such that $\phi(a) = x$. If there is an isomorphism $\phi: R \to R'$, we say that R and R' are **isomorphic.** The two rings R and R' are then, in some sense, the same. The elements of R and the elements of R' can be made to correspond to one another, by the mapping ϕ, so that the elements of one ring add and multiply just like the corresponding elements in the other ring.

Example 42. If R, R' are any two rings, the mapping defined by $\phi(a) = 0$ (the zero element of R'), for all a in R, is a homomorphism. In this case, Im $\phi = \{0\}$ and Ker $\phi = R$.

Example 43. If we take $R' = R$ and define the mapping $\phi : R \to R$ by $\phi(a) = a$, for all a in R, then Im $\phi = R$ and Ker $\phi = \{0\}$, and ϕ is an isomorphism. Admittedly this is rather a trivial one in which each element simply corresponds to itself.

Example 44. A less trivial example of an isomorphism from a ring to itself is the mapping $\phi: J[\sqrt{2}] \to J[\sqrt{2}]$ defined by $\phi(a + b\sqrt{2}) = a - b\sqrt{2}$. The reader should check that Im $\phi = J[\sqrt{2}]$, Ker $\phi = \{0\}$, and that **H1** and **H2** are satisfied.

Example 45. The mapping $\phi : J \to J_n$ defined by $\phi(a) = [a]$ is a homomorphism. **H1** and **H2** are satisfied because of the definitions of addition and multiplication in J_n given on p. 9. Im $\phi = J_n$, so this is an epimorphism, and Ker $\phi = $ the set of all multiples of n.

Example 46. The previous example is a special case of the following very important one: If U is an ideal of a ring R, there is a homomorphism from R to the quotient ring R/U defined by $\phi(a) = [a]$. **H1** and **H2** are satisfied because of the definitions of addition and multiplication in R/U given on page 34. Im ϕ is the whole of R/U so ϕ is an epimorphism and the kernel is the ideal U.

THEOREM 46. *If $\phi: R \to R'$ is a homomorphism,*

(i) *Im ϕ is a subring of R',*

(ii) *Ker ϕ is an ideal of R.*

Proof. (i) Im ϕ is not empty. If x, y are in Im ϕ, then $x = \phi(a)$, $y = \phi(b)$, say. By Theorem 44 (iii), $x - y = \phi(a - b)$, and by **H2**, $xy = \phi(ab)$. It follows that Im ϕ contains $x - y$ and xy, and is thus a subring of R' by Theorem 32.

(ii) Ker ϕ is not empty. If a, b are in Ker ϕ, then $\phi(a) = 0$ and $\phi(b) = 0$. So $\phi(a - b) = \phi(a) - \phi(b) = 0$. Moreover, if r is any element of R, $\phi(ra) = \phi(r)\phi(a) = 0$ and also $\phi(ar) = \phi(a)\phi(r) = 0$. It follows that Ker ϕ contains $a - b$ and ra and ar, for all r in R, and is thus an ideal of R by Theorem 34.

We can now show the very close connection between homomorphisms and quotient rings by proving what is in effect the converse of Example 46:

THEOREM 47. *If $\phi: R \to R'$ is a homomorphism and $K = $ Ker ϕ, then the mapping $\phi^*: R/K \to$ Im ϕ, defined by $\phi^*([a]) = \phi(a)$, is an isomorphism. Thus Im ϕ is isomorphic to the quotient ring R/K.*

Proof. First, the definition of ϕ^* is an unambiguous one, for if $[a] = [b]$, then $a - b$ is in K, so $\phi(a - b) = 0$. Thus $\phi(a) - \phi(b) = 0$, i.e. $\phi(a) = \phi(b)$. Moreover ϕ^* satisfies **H1**, since $\phi^*([a] + [b]) = \phi^*([a + b]) = \phi(a + b) = \phi(a) + \phi(b) = \phi^*([a]) + \phi^*([b])$; the proof of **H2** is similar. ϕ^* is clearly an epimorphism and can be shown to be a monomorphism as follows: If $\phi(a) = \phi(b)$, then $\phi(a - b) = 0$. Hence $a - b$ is in K, and thus $[a] = [b]$.

Exercises for this chapter will be found on p. 72.

D

CHAPTER SIX

Polynomials and Euclidean Rings

25. Polynomials

We have already spoken of a real polynomial as an expression of the form $a_0 + a_1x + a_2x^2 + \ldots + a_nx^n$, where $a_0, a_1, \ldots, a_n$ are real numbers and x is an "indeterminate". We have added and multiplied such expressions without inquiring too deeply into their meaning. In a precise definition, we certainly want two polynomials to be considered equal, or the same, only if the corresponding coefficients are equal. Indeed, a polynomial is determined by its coefficients, so we may define a polynomial as a sequence $(a_0, a_1, a_2, \ldots)$, where only a finite number of the a's are not zero. This may seem an odd definition at first, with no mention of x, but we find that it avoids awkward questions about the nature of x and the validity of writing operations of multiplication like a_1x and addition like $a_0 + a_1x$. The elements a_i may still be called the coefficients, and we shall not limit these to real numbers, but allow them to be elements of any field:

DEFINITION. *A* **polynomial over a field** *F is a sequence $f = (a_0, a_1, a_2, \ldots)$ of elements of F, where only a finite number of the a's are not zero. The* **degree** *of f, denoted by deg f, is the integer n, where a_n is the last non-zero element in the sequence. (The degree of the zero polynomial, with all terms in the sequence zero, is not defined.) The polynomial f is* **monic** *if its last, or highest, coefficient $a_n = 1$.*

We can now define addition and multiplication on the set of all polynomials over F. If $f = (a_0, a_1, a_2, \ldots)$ and $g = (b_0,$

DIVISIBILITY

b_1, b_2, ...), the sum $f + g$ is $(a_0 + b_0, a_1 + b_1, a_2 + b_2, ...)$ and the product fg is $(c_0, c_1, c_2, ...)$, where $c_i = a_0b_i + a_1b_{i-1} + ... + a_ib_0$, for each i. It is left to the reader to show that the set of all polynomials over F with this addition and multiplication is an integral domain $F[x]$, using Example 5 as a guide, if necessary.

We can, if we wish, recover or explain the normal expression for a polynomial in the following way: We may, if there is likely to be no confusion, denote the zero polynomial by 0, and the identity polynomial $(1, 0, 0, ...)$ by 1. Indeed, we may denote the polynomial $(a, 0, 0, ...)$ by a, which is then called a scalar. Suppose now that the polynomial $(0, 1, 0, 0, ...)$ is denoted by x. Then $x^2 = (0, 0, 1, 0, ...)$, $x^3 = (0, 0, 0, 1, 0, ...)$, and so on. We see then, for example, that a_2x^2 stands for $(a_2, 0, 0, ...) (0, 0, 1, 0, ...) = (0, 0, a_2, 0, ...)$, by the rule for multiplication. Thus $f = (a_0, a_1, a_2, ...) = (a_0, 0, 0, ...) + (0, a_1, 0, ...) + (0, 0, a_2, 0, ...) + ... = a_0 + a_1x + a_2x^2 + ...$, where this terminates at some point since only a finite number of the a's are non-zero. Terms with zero coefficients are omitted. In this way, we have put our theory of polynomials on a sound basis, and can use the familiar expressions knowing that, if the need arises, we can return to our rigorous notation.

THEOREM 48. *If neither $f(x)$ nor $g(x)$ is the zero polynomial, $deg\ f(x)g(x) = deg\ f(x) + deg\ g(x)$.*

Proof. If $f(x)$ has a_nx^n as its highest term, and $g(x)$ has b_mx^m as its highest term, then the product $f(x)g(x)$ has $a_nb_mx^{m+n}$ as its highest term, which gives the result. Alternatively we can write: if $f = (a_0, a_1, a_2, ...)$, where a_n is the last non-zero term, and $g = (b_0, b_1, b_2, ...)$, where b_m is the last non-zero term, then $fg = (c_0, c_1, c_2, ...)$ and the last non-zero term is $c_{m+n} = a_nb_m$.

26. Divisibility

Our main intention now is to prove results for polynomials

41

by following closely the work that was done for integers in Chapter 3. We shall show that any polynomial can be written as the product of so-called irreducible factors in essentially only one way. But much of the theory, such as the concept of divisibility, applies equally well in any integral domain:

DEFINITION. *In any integral domain D, a **divides** b if there is an element q in D such that $aq = b$. We write $a \mid b$.*

THEOREM 49.
(i) *If $a \mid b$ and $b \mid c$, then $a \mid c$,*
(ii) *If $a \mid b$, then $ac \mid bc$,*
(iii) *If $a \mid b$ and $a \mid c$, then $a \mid (mb + nc)$, where m and n are any elements of D.*

You can see that the proofs of Theorem 16 hold in any integral domain.

DEFINITION. *In any integral domain, the divisors of 1 are called **units**.*

Example 47. In **J**, the units are ± 1 (see Theorem 17(i)).

Example 48. In $F[x]$, the domain of all polynomials over F, the units are the non-zero scalars: Clearly, any non-zero scalar a is a unit, since a has an inverse a^{-1}, and $a.a^{-1} = 1$ demonstrates that $a \mid 1$. Suppose that the polynomial $a(x) \mid 1$. Then $a(x)q(x) = 1$, for some polynomial $q(x)$, where neither $a(x)$ nor $q(x)$ can be the zero polynomial. Thus $\deg a(x) + \deg q(x) = \deg a(x)q(x) =$ the degree of the identity polynomial $= 0$. Therefore $\deg a(x) = 0$, so $a(x)$ is a non-zero scalar.

Example 49. In $\mathbf{J}[\sqrt{2}]$, if $a + b\sqrt{2}$ is a unit, there is an element $c + d\sqrt{2}$ such that $(a + b\sqrt{2})(c + d\sqrt{2}) = 1$. Then, as in Example 18, $c = a/(a^2 - 2b^2)$ and $d = -b/(a^2 - 2b^2)$. So c and d will certainly be integers if we choose $a^2 - 2b^2 = \pm 1$. There are many possibilities such as $b = 1$, $a = \pm 1$; or $b = 2$, $a = \pm 3$; or $b = 5$, $a = \pm 7$. So 1 has many factorisations like $(1 + \sqrt{2})(-1 + \sqrt{2})$ or $(3 + 2\sqrt{2})(3 - 2\sqrt{2})$ or $(7 + 5\sqrt{2})(-7 + 5\sqrt{2})$, and the factors here are examples of units in $\mathbf{J}[\sqrt{2}]$.

Example 50. The set $\mathbf{J}[i]$ of Gaussian integers $a + bi$, where a and b are integers, is a integral domain; for it is certainly a subring of **C** (see Example 33), and there are no divisors of zero in $\mathbf{J}[i]$ since there are no divisors of zero in **C**. If $a + bi$ is a unit, then a, b are not both zero, and there is an element $c + di$ such that $(a + bi)(c + di) = 1$. Thus $ac - bd = 1$ and $bc + ad = 0$, which give $c = a/(a^2 + b^2)$, $d = -b/(a^2 + b^2)$.

Now $a^2 + b^2$ is a positive integer n, say, so if c and d are to be integers, a and b must be divisible by n. Let $a = nx$, $b = ny$, and then $n^2x^2 + n^2y^2 = n$. Therefore $n(x^2 + y^2) = 1$, and so $n = 1$, i.e. $a^2 + b^2 = 1$. The possible values are $a = \pm 1$, $b = 0$; or $a = 0$, $b = \pm 1$. Thus the units in $J[i]$ are 1, -1, i, $-i$.

THEOREM 50. *If $a \mid b$ and $b \mid a$, then $a = ub$, where u is a unit.*
Proof. If $a \mid b$ and $b \mid a$, then $ac = b$ and $bd = a$. Therefore $acd = a$, and so $cd = 1$. Thus d is a unit, which gives the result.

DEFINITION. *If $a \mid b$ and $b \mid a$, a is an* **associate** *of b.*

27. Euclidean Rings

We shall continue to develop a theory parallel to that of Chapter 3 in as general a situation as possible, but we now have to restrict ourselves to integral domains in which a division algorithm like that for integers holds. We give a new name to these:

DEFINITION. *An integral domain D is called a* **Euclidean ring** *if there is a non-negative integer $\nu(a)$ corresponding to each non-zero element a, such that*

(i) *if a, b are non-zero, $\nu(ab) \geq \nu(a)$,*
(ii) *for any two elements a, b with $b \neq 0$, there are elements q and r in D such that $a = bq + r$, where either $r = 0$, or $\nu(r) < \nu(b)$.*

Example 51. J is a Euclidean ring, where $\nu(a)$ is $|a|$: (i) holds because, by Theorem 11, $|ab| = |a|.|b| \geqslant |a|$, since $|b| > 0$. Moreover, if $b > 0$, from Theorem 18, there are integers q, r such that $a = bq + r$ where $0 \leqslant r < b$; whereas if $b < 0$, the proof of that theorem can quite easily be adapted to show that there are integers q, r such that $a = bq + r$ where $b < r \leqslant 0$. These two combine to give the property (ii) required.

Example 52. The set $J[i]$ of Gaussian integers is a Euclidean ring: The definition of modulus $|z|$ of a complex number is familiar, and it has the properties that $|z| \geqslant 0$ for all z, with $|z| = 0$ if and only if $z = 0$, and $|z_1 z_2| = |z_1| . |z_2|$. For any non-zero Gaussian integer x, we define $\nu(x) = |x|^2$, and from the property for modulus we can deduce that $\nu(xy) = \nu(x) . \nu(y)$. Alternatively, for $x = a + bi$, you can define $\nu(x) = a^2 + b^2$ and use direct calculation. Then if x, y are non-zero, $\nu(y) \geqslant 1$, so $\nu(xy) \geqslant \nu(x)$ as required for a Euclidean ring.

43

POLYNOMIALS AND EUCLIDEAN RINGS

If, given x and y, we want to find elements q and r such that $x = qy + r$, we notice that we should have $r = x - qy = y(x/y - q)$, where x/y is a complex number not necessarily a Gaussian integer. Extending the function ν so that $\nu(z) = |z|^2$ for any complex number z, $\nu(r) = \nu(y).\nu(x/y - q)$, so $\nu(r) < \nu(y)$ if $\nu(x/y - q) < 1$. Represent x/y by the point P on the Argand diagram, and let Q be a point, representing a Gaussian integer q, nearest to P. The Gaussian integers lie at the points with integer coordinates and so the distance of any point from one of these is at most half the length

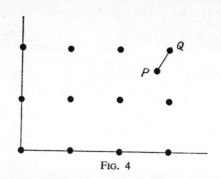

FIG. 4

of the diagonal of a unit square. Thus $|x/y - q| \leqslant (\sqrt{2})/2 = 1/\sqrt{2}$, and so $\nu(x/y - q) \leqslant 1/2 < 1$. This element q and the element $r = x - qy$, which is either zero or has $\nu(r) < \nu(y)$, are the required quotient and remainder.

Example 53. $F[x]$ is a Euclidean ring, where $\nu(a)$ is the degree of the polynomial a. The proof of this consists of the following two theorems.

THEOREM 51. *If neither $a(x)$ nor $b(x)$ is the zero polynomial, then deg $a(x)b(x) \geq deg\ a(x)$.*

Proof. From Theorem 48, deg $a(x)b(x) = $ deg $a(x) + $ deg $b(x)$ $\geq$ deg $a(x)$, since deg $b(x) \geq 0$.

THEOREM 52 (**The Division Algorithm for Polynomials**). *For given polynomials $a(x)$ and $b(x)$, with $b(x) \neq 0$, there exist unique polynomials $q(x)$ and $r(x)$ such that $a(x) = b(x)q(x) + r(x)$, where either $r(x) = 0$ or deg $r(x) < $ deg $b(x)$.*

Proof. If deg $a(x) < $ deg $b(x)$, we may take $q(x) = 0$ and $r(x) = a(x)$. Suppose that deg $a(x) \geq$ deg $b(x)$, and let $a(x) = a_0 + a_1x + ... + a_nx^n$, and $b(x) = b_0 + b_1x + ... + b_mx^m$.

We subtract from $a(x)$ a suitable multiple of $b(x)$ so that the highest term of $a(x)$ is eliminated, giving

$$a(x) - b(x) \cdot (a_n/b_m)x^{n-m} = \text{some polynomial of degree less than deg } a(x).$$

If the polynomial on the right hand side still has degree $\geq$ deg $b(x)$, we subtract another suitable multiple of $b(x)$ so that the highest term again disappears. Thus eventually

$$a(x) - b(x)[(a_n/b_m)x^{n-m} + \ldots] = r(x),$$

where either $r(x) = 0$ or deg $r(x) <$ deg $b(x)$. So we get $a(x) - b(x)q(x) = r(x)$, i.e. $a(x) = b(x)q(x) + r(x)$, as required.

The proof really uses the Second Principle of Induction, where $P(n)$ is the proposition "a polynomial of degree n can be written as $b(x)q(x) + r(x)$, where either $r(x) = 0$ or deg $r(x) <$ deg $b(x)$." We can see that the proposition is true for sufficiently small n, less than deg $b(x)$. Now take $a(x)$ of degree n, as above, and write

$$a(x) - b(x) \cdot (a_n/b_m)x^{n-m} = \text{some polynomial of degree } < n.$$

We may use the induction hypothesis to suppose that the polynomial on the right hand side may be written $b(x)q'(x) + r'(x)$, where $r'(x)$ is either zero or deg $r'(x) <$ deg $b(x)$. Then

$$a(x) = b(x)[(a_n/b_m)x^{n-m} + q'(x)] + r'(x),$$

giving $a(x)$ itself in the required form.

We leave the reader to show that the quotient and remainder are unique, using Theorem 18 as a guide, if necessary. In the case of polynomials, you will need to use Theorem 51 where Theorem 17(iii) was quoted in the case of integers.

The first important and useful property that we can show that a Euclidean ring has is this:

THEOREM 53. *In a Euclidean ring, every ideal is a principal ideal.*

Proof. If U is an ideal and $U \neq \{0\}$, let d be a non-zero element of U with $v(d)$ as small as possible for elements of U.

If a is any element of U, write $a = dq + r$, where either $r = 0$ or $v(r) < v(d)$. Then $r = a - dq$, and so r is in U. However $v(r) < v(d)$ would contradict the choice of d as having $v(d)$ as small as possible. So $r = 0$. Hence $a = qd$, i.e. every element of U is a multiple of d. Therefore U is the principal ideal (d).

28. Highest Common Factor

The concept of highest common factor can be defined in any integral domain:

DEFINITION. *In an integral domain D, an element d of D is a* **highest common factor** *of the two elements, a, b of D if $d \mid a$ and $d \mid b$, and if $x \mid a$ and $x \mid b$ imply that $x \mid d$. We write $d = (a, b)$.*

In the general case, a highest common factor may not exist for some or all pairs of elements, and even if one does exist it certainly need not be unique. In a Euclidean ring, however, the situation is quite straightforward:

THEOREM 54. *In a Euclidean ring D, any two elements, a, b have a highest common factor d in D, which can be expressed as $sa + tb$, where s, t are in D. Any two h.c.fs. of a and b are associates.*

Proof. Let U be the set of all elements $ha + kb$, where h, k are in D; then U is an ideal, and by Theorem 53, is a principal ideal (d). But a and b belong to U, so a and b are multiples of d, i.e. $d \mid a$ and $d \mid b$. Since d is a member of U, d can be expressed as $sa + tb$, say. So, if $x \mid a$ and $x \mid b$, then $x \mid (sa + tb)$, by Theorem 49(iii), i.e. $x \mid d$. Therefore d is an h.c.f. of a and b. If d and d' are both h.c.fs. of a and b, then $d \mid a$ and $d \mid b$, so $d \mid d'$ because d' is an h.c.f. But similarly $d' \mid d$. Therefore d and d' are associates.

Example 54. In **J**, d is an associate of d' if and only if $d = \pm d'$, so any two integers have a unique *positive* h.c.f.

Example 55. In $F[x]$, $d(x)$ is an associate of $d'(x)$ if and only if $d(x) = c.d'(x)$, where c is a non-zero scalar, so any two polynomials have a unique *monic* (see p. 40) h.c.f.

IRREDUCIBLE ELEMENTS

Example 56. We can use Euclid's Algorithm, described on p. 20 for integers, to find the h.c.f. of two elements $x = 5i$ and $y = 3 + i$, say, of $J[i]$. First, we must find elements q and r such that $x = yq + r$, with $v(r) < v(y)$. Following Example 52, we work out $x/y = 5i/(3 + i) = 5i(3 - i)/10 = (1 + 3i)/2$. So we choose a Gaussian integer nearest to it, $q = i$ (say) and $r = x - qy = 5i - i(3 + i) = 1 + 2i$. Therefore, $5i = i(3 + i) + (1 + 2i)$. Now take the two elements $3 + i$ and $1 + 2i$, and find a quotient and remainder: $(3 + i)/(1 + 2i) = (3 + i)(1 - 2i)/5 = (5 - 5i)/5 = 1 - i$, so $(3 + i) = (1 + 2i)(1 - i)$, with no remainder. Therefore, the h.c.f., $(5i, 3 + i) = (3 + i, 1 + 2i) = 1 + 2i$. The associates of this, $-1 - 2i$, $-2 + i$, $2 - i$, are also h.c.fs. of the given Gaussian integers.

29. Irreducible elements

DEFINITION. *In a Euclidean ring, an element is* **irreducible** *if it is not a unit and if its only divisors are its associates and the units.*

An element is always divisible by its associates and by all the units; divisors other than these are called **proper** divisors. So an irreducible element is one with no proper divisors.

Example 57. In **J**, the irreducible elements are the primes and their negatives.

Example 58. In $F[x]$, a polynomial is irreducible if it has degree > 0, and its only divisors are scalars and scalar multiples of itself. The polynomial $x^2 - 2$, for example, is an element of $R[x]$ and can be written $x^2 - 2 = (x - \sqrt{2})(x + \sqrt{2})$, so $x - \sqrt{2}$ and $x + \sqrt{2}$ are proper divisors. Thus $x^2 - 2$ is not irreducible. But considering the same polynomial as an element of $Q[x]$ instead, it is irreducible because it has no proper factors with *rational* coefficients. We say that $x^2 - 2$ is irreducible over **Q**. Similarly, considered as an element of $C[x]$, $x^2 + 1 = (x + i)(x - i)$, but $x^2 + 1$ has no proper factors with *real* coefficients. So $x^2 + 1$ is irreducible over **R**.

DEFINITION. *In a Euclidean ring, two elements are* **relatively prime** *if they have a unit as an h.c.f.*

If a and b are relatively prime, all the units, including the identity element, are h.c.fs. of a and b, so we may write $(a, b) = 1$. It is an easy matter to see that the following theorems can be proved in the same way as they were for integers.

THEOREM 55. *In a Euclidean ring, if $(a, b) = 1$, and $a \mid bc$, then $a \mid c$.*

47

POLYNOMIALS AND EUCLIDEAN RINGS

THEOREM 56. *If p is an irreducible element of a Euclidean ring*
(i) $p \mid ab$ only if $p \mid a$ or $p \mid b$,
(ii) $p \mid a_1 a_2 \ldots a_n$ *implies* $p \mid a_i$ *for some i.*

Since $F[x]$ is a Euclidean ring, we know that every ideal in
$F[x]$ is a principal ideal. Following the proof of Theorem 53,
the ideal U is in fact the principal ideal generated by any
polynomial $f(x)$ in U with degree as small as possible. The
following theorem shows how irreducible polynomials play the
role taken by primes in the theory for integers.

THEOREM 57. *The ideal* $(f(x))$ *of* $F[x]$ *is maximal if and only if*
$f(x)$ *is irreducible.*

The proof, which is similar to Example 41, is left as an
exercise.

30. Unique Factorisation

First, two results about units in Euclidean rings, and then
we can prove the Unique Factorisation Theorem:

THEOREM 58. *In a Euclidean ring*
(i) *if c is not a unit*, $v(b) < v(bc)$,
(ii) *a is a unit if and only if* $v(a) = v(1)$.

Proof. (i) Let U be the principal ideal (b). Then $v(b) \leq v(bx)$
for all x, so $v(b) \leq v(a)$ for all a in U. If $v(b) = v(bc)$, then
$v(bc) \leq v(a)$ for all a in U, so, as in Theorem 53, U is also the
ideal generated by bc. Therefore, b itself is a multiple of bc,
i.e. $b = bcy$. Then $cy = 1$ and so c is a unit. Thus, if c is not a
unit, we can say that $v(b) < v(bc)$.

(ii) Certainly, for any element a, $v(1) \leq v(1a) = v(a)$. If a is
a unit, there is an element b such that $ab = 1$. Then $v(a) \leq
v(ab) = v(1)$, so $v(a) = v(1)$. Conversely, if $v(a) = v(1)$, we can
write this as $v(1) = v(1a)$. It follows from (i) that a is a unit.

THEOREM 59 (**The Unique Factorisation Theorem**). *In a*
Euclidean ring, any element is either a unit or can be written

48

uniquely (up to associates) as the product of a finite number of irreducible elements.

Proof. The proof is essentially that given for integers but translated into language which is appropriate for any Euclidean ring. Let $P(n)$ be the proposition "any element a with $\nu(a) = n$ is either a unit or can be written as the product of a finite number of irreducible elements."

If $\nu(a) = \nu(1)$, then a is a unit, so $P(n)$ is true for $n = \nu(1)$. Suppose that a is an element with $\nu(a) = n > \nu(1)$. If a is irreducible, it is the product of a finite number of irreducible elements. If not, then $a = bc$, where neither b nor c is a unit or an associate of a. So $\nu(b) < \nu(a)$ and $\nu(c) < \nu(a)$, by Theorem 58(i). Assuming that the proposition is true for all values of n less than $\nu(a)$, we know that b and c can each be written as the product of a finite number of irreducible elements, and we may deduce that the same is true for a. By the Second Principle of Induction, the proposition is true for all possible values of $\nu(a)$.

To prove the uniqueness (up to associates), suppose that $p_1 p_2 \ldots p_r = q_1 q_2 \ldots q_s$, where $p_1, \ldots, p_r, q_1, \ldots, q_s$ are irreducible. Then $p_1 \mid q_1 q_2 \ldots q_s$, and so $p_1 \mid q_i$ for some i. Since each is irreducible, they must be associates. Writing $q_i = u p_1$, where u is a unit, and cancelling p_1 from both sides, we continue similarly with p_2 and so on, and show that $r = s$ and that $q_1, \ldots, q_s$ are just associates of $p_1, \ldots, p_r$ in possibly a different order.

31. Polynomials with Integer Coefficients

Since the integers do not form a field, what we have said about $F[x]$ does not necessarily apply, but it is easy to see that the set $\mathbf{J}[x]$ of polynomials with integer coefficients is an integral domain. It is not a Euclidean ring, however, because the division algorithm breaks down. Our main intention is to show that if a polynomial with integer coefficients cannot be factorised using integer coefficients, then you cannot factorise it with rational coefficients.

DEFINITION. *A polynomial in* $\mathbf{Q}[x]$ *is* **primitive** *if it has integer coefficients and the coefficients have h.c.f.* 1.

THEOREM 60. *The product of two primitive polynomials is primitive.*

Proof. Suppose that $f(x) = a_0 + a_1x + \ldots + a_nx^n$ and $g(x) = b_0 + b_1x + \ldots + b_mx^m$ are primitive, and $f(x)g(x)$ is not primitive. The coefficients of $f(x)g(x)$, which are integers, must have h.c.f. greater than 1, so there is a prime p dividing all the coefficients. Now, p does not divide all the coefficients of $f(x)$, so let a_i be the first coefficient of $f(x)$ that p does not divide. Similarly, let b_j be the first coefficient of $g(x)$ that p does not divide. Then $c_{i+j} = a_0b_{i+j} + \ldots + a_ib_j + \ldots + a_{i+j}b_0$ is a coefficient in $f(x)g(x)$. But $p \mid c_{i+j}$, and p divides $a_0, \ldots, a_{i-1}$ and $b_0, \ldots, b_{j-1}$, so $p \mid a_ib_j$. This implies either $p \mid a_i$ or $p \mid b_j$ which is a contradiction showing that $f(x)g(x)$ is primitive.

THEOREM 61. *Any non-zero polynomial* $f(x)$, *with rational coefficients, can be written as* $f(x) = c_f f^*(x)$, *where* c_f *is a positive rational number and* $f^*(x)$ *is primitive. For a given polynomial* $f(x)$, *the number* c_f, *which is the* **content** *of* $f(x)$, *and the primitive polynomial* $f^*(x)$ *are unique.*

Proof. Let k be any positive integer which is divisible by all the denominators of the rationals occuring as coefficients of $f(x)$. Then $f(x)$ is equal to $1/k$ times a polynomial with integer coefficients. If h is the positive h.c.f. of these integer coefficients, $f(x)$ is equal to h/k times a primitive polynomial as required. To prove the uniqueness, suppose that $a.f(x) = b.g(x)$, where a, b are positive rational numbers, and $f(x)$, $g(x)$ are primitive. We can write $g(x) = (a/b)f(x)$ where a/b is a positive rational number m/n, say, where m, n are positive *integers* with h.c.f. 1. Then $g(x) = (m/n)f(x)$, or $m.f(x) = n.g(x)$. If $m > 1$, m has a prime factor p which does not divide n, so divides every coefficient of $g(x)$. This is not so, since $g(x)$ is primitive, so $m = 1$. Similarly $n = 1$, and $f(x) = g(x)$ and $a = b$, which proves the uniqueness.

THEOREM 62. *If $f(x) = g(x)h(x)$, where each of these has rational coefficients, then $f^*(x) = g^*(x)h^*(x)$ and $c_f = c_g c_h$.*

Proof. Writing $f(x) = c_f f^*(x)$ etc., $c_f f^*(x) = f(x) = g(x)h(x) = c_g c_h g^*(x)h^*(x)$. But $g^*(x)h^*(x)$ is primitive by Theorem 60, and $c_g c_h > 0$, so, by the uniqueness established in the last theorem, $f^*(x) = g^*(x)h^*(x)$ and $c_f = c_g c_h$.

THEOREM 63. *A polynomial with integer coefficients which can be factorised into polynomials with rational coefficients can be factorised into polynomials with integer coefficients, where the polynomials in the second factorisation are scalar multiples of those in the first.*

Proof. If $f(x)$ has integer coefficients, c_f is an integer. Now, if $f(x) = g(x)h(x)$ is a factorisation using rationals, $f(x) = c_g c_h g^*(x)h^*(x) = c_f g^*(x)h^*(x)$, as in the last theorem. This is a factorisation using integers, since c_f is an integer and $g^*(x)$, $h^*(x)$ have integer coefficients. The two factors $c_f g^*(x)$ and $h^*(x)$ are scalar multiples of the original factors.

The last theorem implies that if $f(x)$ is irreducible over **J**, it is irreducible over **Q**. This is useful in finding whether a polynomial is irreducible over **Q**, as possible factors with integer coefficients are often easily recognised.

Example 59. $8x^3 - 6x - 1$ is irreducible over **Q**: If this polynomial had proper factors, one must be of degree 1. But $(ax + b)(cx^2 + dx + e) = 8x^3 - 6x - 1$ implies $ac = 8$, $be = -1$, so if a, b are integers, $a \mid 8$, $b \mid -1$. Thus the only possible linear factors with integer coefficients are $x \pm 1$, $2x \pm 1$, $4x \pm 1$ and $8x \pm 1$. Trying, for example, $x + 1$, we have $c = 8$, $e = -1$, but no value for d gives the right result. In this way, we find that the polynomial is irreducible over **J** and hence over **Q**.

Example 60. If p is any prime, $x^2 - p$ has no factors with integer coefficients, so it is irreducible over **Q**. The factorisation $(x - \sqrt{p})(x + \sqrt{p})$ cannot therefore have rational coefficients, so $\sqrt{p}$ is irrational for any prime p.

Exercises for this chapter will be found on p. 74.

CHAPTER SEVEN

Vector Spaces

---

32. Definition of a Vector Space

Vectors are commonly defined to be quantities that have direction as well as magnitude. For any two such **arrows**, as we shall call them, **a** and **b**, through a fixed point, their sum **a** + **b** is defined by the parallelogram rule. Any arrow **a** may also be multiplied by a scalar c to give an arrow c**a**.

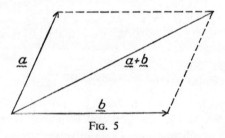

Fig. 5

The set of n-vectors has similar properties. An **n-vector** is a row $\mathbf{x} = (x_1, ..., x_n)$ of n numbers, and given two n-vectors, **x** and $\mathbf{y} = (y_1, ..., y_n)$, their sum $\mathbf{x} + \mathbf{y}$ is defined to be the n-vector $(x_1+y_1, ..., x_n+y_n)$. If c is a scalar, $c\mathbf{x}$ is defined to be $(cx_1, ..., cx_n)$. The similarity between the set of arrows through a point, and the set of n-vectors, and the existence of other sets with addition and "multiplication by scalars", but not "true" multiplication, leads us to make the following definition:

DEFINITION. *A* **vector space** *V over a field F is a set of elements, called* **vectors**, *closed under addition (so that any two vectors α and β determine a vector $\alpha + \beta$) and closed under multiplication*

52

DEFINITION OF A VECTOR SPACE

by elements of F (so that any vector α and element c of F determine a vector cα) with these properties:

V1. $\alpha + \beta = \beta + \alpha$, *for all* α, β *in* V,

V2. $\alpha + (\beta + \gamma) = (\alpha + \beta) + \gamma$, *for all* α, β, γ *in* V,

V3. *There is a zero element* **0** *such that* $\alpha + 0 = \alpha$, *for all* α *in* V.

V4. *For each* α *in* V, *there is a negative* $(-\alpha)$ *such that* $\alpha + (-\alpha) = 0$,

V5. $(c + d)\alpha = c\alpha + d\alpha$, *for all* α *in* V *and* c, d *in* F,

V6. $c(\alpha + \beta) = c\alpha + c\beta$, *for all* α, β *in* V *and* c *in* F,

V7. $(cd)\alpha = c(d\alpha)$, *for all* α *in* V *and* c, d *in* F,

V8. $1\alpha = \alpha$, *for all* α *in* V.

The vectors will be denoted by greek letters, and the elements of F, called **scalars,** *by roman letters.*

The following elementary results can be deduced from **V1** to **V8**:

THEOREM 64. *In any vector space*

(i) *if* $\alpha + \beta = \alpha$, *then* $\beta = 0$,

(ii) *Each element has a unique negative,*

(iii) $0\alpha = 0$, *for all* α,

(iv) $c0 = 0$, *for all* c,

(v) $-\alpha = (-1)\alpha$, *for all* α,

(vi) $c\alpha = 0$ *only if either* $c = 0$ *or* $\alpha = 0$.

Proof. (i) If $\alpha + \beta = \alpha$, then $(\alpha + \beta) + (-\alpha) = \alpha + (-\alpha) = 0$. But also $(\alpha + \beta) + (-\alpha) = (\beta + \alpha) + (-\alpha)$ (by **V1**) $= \beta + (\alpha + (-\alpha))$ (by **V2**) $= \beta + 0 = \beta$. Thus $\beta = 0$.

(ii) Let $(-\alpha)$ be a negative of α, and suppose also that $\alpha + \beta = 0$. Adding $(-\alpha)$ to both sides gives $\beta = (-\alpha)$. So α has a unique negative.

(iii) $\alpha + 0\alpha = 1\alpha + 0\alpha = (1 + 0)\alpha = 1\alpha = \alpha$. Therefore, $0\alpha = 0$ by (i).

(iv) $c\alpha + c0 = c(\alpha + 0) = c\alpha$. Therefore $c0 = 0$, by (i).

(v) $\alpha + (-1)\alpha = 1\alpha + (-1)\alpha = (1 + (-1))\alpha = 0\alpha = 0$, by (iii). Therefore $(-1)\alpha = -\alpha$, by (ii).

(vi) Given $c\alpha = \mathbf{0}$. If $c \neq 0$, then c has an inverse c^{-1}. Then $c^{-1}(c\alpha) = c^{-1}\mathbf{0} = \mathbf{0}$. Hence $(c^{-1}c)\alpha = \mathbf{0}$, and so $1\alpha = \mathbf{0}$, i.e. $\alpha = \mathbf{0}$. Therefore either $c = 0$ or $\alpha = \mathbf{0}$.

Example 61. The set of all arrows through a point in 3 dimensions is a vector space over **R**. The vector space in this case is over **R** since the scalars that we are allowed to multiply by are the real numbers.

Example 62. If we take the set of all *n*-vectors $\mathbf{x} = (x_1, ..., x_n)$, where $x_1, ..., x_n$ belong to a field F, addition and multiplication by scalars can be defined as above to give a vector space over F. We shall denote this important example† by $V_n(F)$.

Example 63. The set $F[x]$ of all polynomials over F is a vector space over F. In this case, we ignore the fact that we can multiply two polynomials together. All we require is the addition and the multiplication of polynomials by scalars. This being so, the set of all polynomials with coefficients in F which have degree $<$ some fixed number n, also form a vector space over F, for this smaller set is closed under these two operations, though not under "true" multiplication.

Example 64. If F is a subfield of a field K, then K is a vector space over F. In this example, we take the elements of K as the vectors, and the elements of the subfield F as scalars. We can certainly add two vectors together (using the addition in K); we ignore the multiplication between the elements of K, except for the multiplication of an element of K by an element of the subfield F, which gives us the multiplication by scalars. By considering a field in this light, and applying results about vector spaces, we can discover more about the structure of fields.

For example, we may consider **C** as a vector space over **R**. The complex numbers are the vectors and the real numbers are the scalars.

33. Definition of a Basis

DEFINITION. *The vector space V over a field F is* **generated** *by the elements $\xi_1, ..., \xi_m$ if every element of V is a linear combination $c_1\xi_1 + ... + c_m\xi_m$, where $c_1, ..., c_m$ are in F.*

There is another concept very closely linked with the idea of one vector being a linear combination of others: we shall say that a set of vectors is *linearly dependent* if one of them is a linear combination of the others. Or, to put it another way:

---

† A great deal more about *n*-vectors will be found in *Linear Equations* by P. M. Cohn, in this Library.

DEFINITION OF A BASIS

DEFINITION. *The set of vectors $\xi_1, ..., \xi_m$ of a vector space V over a field F is* **linearly dependent (l.d.)** *if there are scalars $c_1, ..., c_m$ in F, not all zero, such that $c_1\xi_1 + ... + c_m\xi_m = 0$. Otherwise the set is* **linearly independent (l.i.).**

Certainly if ξ_m is a linear combination of $\xi_1, ..., \xi_{m-1}$, then $\xi_m = c_1\xi_1 + ... + c_{m-1}\xi_{m-1}$, so $c_1\xi_1 + ... + c_{m-1}\xi_{m-1} + (-1)\xi_m = 0$. Thus $\xi_1, ..., \xi_m$ are l.d. according to the definition. Conversely, we can show that if a set of vectors is l.d. then one of them is a linear combination of the others. We can actually prove something slightly stronger:

THEOREM 65. *If the non-zero vectors $\xi_1, ..., \xi_m$, given in a fixed order, are l.d., then one of them is a linear combination of the preceding ones.*

Proof. If $c_1\xi_1 + ... + c_m\xi_m = 0$, let c_k be the last non-zero coefficient. Then $k \neq 1$, otherwise we have $c_1\xi_1 = 0$, with $c_1 \neq 0$, which implies $\xi_1 = 0$, which is not so. So $\xi_k = (c_k^{-1}c_1)\xi_1 + ... + (c_k^{-1}c_{k-1})\xi_{k-1}$, giving ξ_k as a linear combination of preceding ones.

Any set including the zero vector 0 is l.d. for $0, \xi_1, ..., \xi_m$ satisfy the relation $1.0 + 0\xi_1 + ... + 0\xi_m = 0$, where not all the coefficients are zero. This trick of inserting zero coefficients can also be used to show that if $\xi_1, ..., \xi_m$ are l.d. then any set of vectors including these is l.d. It follows that any subset of a l.i. set is l.i.

Now suppose that a set $\xi_1, ..., \xi_m$ generate a space V, then V consists of all linear combinations of $\xi_1, ..., \xi_m$. If the set is l.d., one of them is a linear combination of the others, and any element of V can be written as a linear combination of the original vectors omitting this one. Thus a set of $m - 1$ vectors generates V. If these are still l.d., we can again write one as a linear combination of the others, and so omit this one. In this way, we shall eventually obtain a l.i. set of vectors which generates V. This technique is used in the next theorem.

E

VECTOR SPACES

THEOREM 66. *Let n vectors generate a vector space V, and suppose that V contains a set of r l.i. vectors. Then $n \geq r$.*

Proof. Suppose $\alpha_1, ..., \alpha_n$ generate V, and $\xi_1, ..., \xi_r$ are l.i.; ξ_1 is a linear combination of $\alpha_1 ..., \alpha_n$, so the set $\xi_1, \alpha_1, ..., \alpha_n$ is l.d. and one of them is a linear combination of the preceding ones. (Notice the order in which we chose to put them.) This one cannot be ξ_1, so it is α_i, say. Using part of the technique just described, we can omit α_i and the set that is left still generates V. Therefore ξ_2 is a linear combination of these, so $\xi_2, \xi_1, \alpha_1, ..., \alpha_{i-1}, \alpha_{i+1}, ..., \alpha_r$ are l.d. Again, one of them is a linear combination of the preceding ones, and it cannot be ξ_1, nor ξ_2 since ξ_1 and ξ_2 are l.i. Omitting whichever α_h it is, gives a new set which generates V, consisting of ξ_1, ξ_2 and $n-2$ of the vectors $\alpha_1, ..., \alpha_n$. After p such steps, we obtain a set which generates V, consisting of $\xi_1, ..., \xi_p$ and $n-p$ of the vectors $\alpha_1, ..., \alpha_n$.

Suppose that $n < r$. Then when $p = n$, the set obtained which generates V consists of $\xi_1, ..., \xi_n$, and there is still at least one more element ξ_{n+1} which is therefore a linear combination of these. But $\xi_1, ..., \xi_{n+1}$ are l.i., and this contradiction shows that $n \geq r$.

DEFINITION. *A **basis** of a vector space V is a l.i. set of vectors which generate V. A vector space is **finite-dimensional** if it has a finite basis.*

34. Dimension

A set of vectors is a basis if it has two properties: it has to generate V (there must be "enough" vectors in the basis to do this); it must be l.i. (there must not be "too many" vectors). The last theorem has an important consequence. If there is a basis with m elements and another with n elements, the first set generate V, and the second set is l.i., so $m \geq n$. But the theorem can be applied to the two sets the other way round

56

DIMENSION

to give $n \geq m$. Thus $m = n$. In other words, in a finite-dimensional vector space, any two bases have the same number of elements. So we can make this definition:

DEFINITION. *The number of elements in any basis of a finite-dimensional vector space V is the* **dimension** *of V, denoted by* dim V.

Example 65. The set of all arrows through a point in 3 dimensions is a vector space of dimension 3. Three arrows are l.d. if and only if they lie in the same plane. Thus any three arrows not in the same plane form a basis.

Example 66. $V_n(F)$ has dimension n. The vectors $e_1 = (1, 0, 0, ..., 0)$, $e_2 = (0, 1, 0, ..., 0)$, ..., $e_n = (0, 0, ..., 1)$ generate $V_n(F)$ since any n-vector $x = (x_1, x_2, ..., x_n)$ is equal to $x_1e_1 + x_2e_2 + ... + x_ne_n$. Moreover, $e_1, ..., e_n$ are l.i. since $c_1e_1 + c_2e_2 + ... + c_ne_n = 0$ implies that $(c_1, c_2, ..., c_n) = (0, 0, ..., 0)$, and so all the coefficients are zero. Thus $e_1, e_2, ..., e_n$ form a basis. There are of course many other bases for the same space, but this one is extremely useful and can be called the **natural** basis for $V_n(F)$.

Example 67. The set of all polynomials over F, of degree $< n$, is a vector space of dimension n. The polynomials $1, x, x^2, ..., x^{n-1}$ can be shown to form a basis. If polynomials are written as sequences as on p. 40, the great similarity between this vector space and $V_n(F)$ becomes apparent. The vector space of *all* polynomials over F is not finite-dimensional.

Example 68. **C**, considered as a vector space over **R**, has dimension 2. Any complex number can be written $a + bi$, where a, b are real, so the two complex numbers $1, i$ generate **C**. Moreover, 1 and i are l.i., since $a + bi = 0$ implies $a = b = 0$. Therefore there is a basis of two elements. There are of course other bases: any two complex numbers neither of which is a real multiple of the other form a basis.

THEOREM 67. *If* dim $V = n$,
 (i) *any l.i. set of vectors is part of a basis*,
 (ii) *any set of $n + 1$ vectors is l.d.*,
 (iii) *no set of $n - 1$ vectors generates V*,
 (iv) *a set of n vectors is a basis if they generate V*,
 (v) *a set of n vectors is a basis if they are l.i.*

Proof. (i) If $\xi_1, ..., \xi_r$ are l.i., take a basis $\alpha_1, ..., \alpha_n$ and consider the set $\xi_1, ..., \xi_r, \alpha_1, ..., \alpha_n$. They generate V, and are l.d., so one of them, which must be one of the α's, is a linear combination of the preceding ones. Using the technique described on p. 55, we can omit this one and continue like this

VECTOR SPACES

until eventually we get a l.i. set which still generates V and includes all the original $\xi_1, ..., \xi_r$.

(ii) If the given $n + 1$ vectors were l.i., they would form part of a basis which would have $\geq n + 1$ elements in it, which is impossible as all bases have n elements.

(iii) If a given set of $n - 1$ vectors generated V, there would be a l.i. subset also generating V, which would be a basis with $\leq n - 1$ elements, which is impossible.

(iv) Any n vectors which generate V have a l.i. subset generating the same space. If this were a proper subset, it would be a basis with $< n$ elements. Therefore the original set of n vectors must be l.i. and form a basis.

(v) Any n l.i. vectors form part of a basis. But a basis cannot have more than n elements, so the n l.i. vectors themselves form a basis.

35. Coordinates

The importance of choosing a l.i. set of vectors which generates V, is that any element of V can be written as a linear combination of them *in a unique way*: if $\alpha_1, ..., \alpha_n$ is a basis, any element ξ can be written $\xi = x_1\alpha_1 + ... + x_n\alpha_n$, because the α's generate V. Now suppose that ξ could be written like this in two ways i.e. $\xi = x_1\alpha_1 + ... + x_n\alpha_n = x_1'\alpha_1 + ... + x_n'\alpha_n$. Then $(x_1 - x_1')\alpha_1 + ... + (x_n - x_n')\alpha_n = \mathbf{0}$. The coefficients $x_1 - x_1', ..., x_n - x_n'$ are all zero because the α's are l.i. Thus $x_1 = x_1', ..., x_n = x_n'$, and the expression for ξ is unique.

DEFINITION. *If* $\xi = x_1\alpha_1 + ... + x_n\alpha_n$, *then* $x_1, ..., x_n$ *are the* **coordinates** *of ξ with respect to the basis* $\alpha_1, ..., \alpha_n$.

Exercises for this chapter will be found on p. 75.

CHAPTER EIGHT

Field Extensions

36. The Degree of a Field Extension

The method of considering a field as a vector space over a subfield will be a powerful one in our further study of fields. We shall now restrict ourselves to working within the complex numbers, so in this chapter all fields mentioned are subfields of **C**.

DEFINITION. *If F is a subfield of a field K, K is an* **extension** *of F. K may be considered as a vector space over F; if this vector space is finite-dimensional, the* **degree of** *K* **over** *F, denoted by* $[K:F]$, *is the dimension of the vector space, and K is a* **finite** *extension of F.*

Example 69. **C** is a finite extension of **R**, and $[\mathbf{C}:\mathbf{R}] = 2$, from Example 68.

Example 70. $\mathbf{Q}(\sqrt{2})$ (see Example 22) is a finite extension of **Q**, and $[\mathbf{Q}(\sqrt{2}):\mathbf{Q}] = 2$, since 1 and $\sqrt{2}$ form a basis for $\mathbf{Q}(\sqrt{2})$ over **Q**.

THEOREM 68. *If L, K and F are fields and $L \supseteq K \supseteq F$, and $[L:K]$ and $[K:F]$ are finite, then $[L:F] = [L:K][K:F]$.*

Proof. Let $[L:K] = m$, and $\alpha_1, ..., \alpha_m$ be a basis for L over K, and let $[K:F] = n$, and $\beta_1, ..., \beta_n$ be a basis for K over F. Any element ξ of L may be written $\xi = c_1\alpha_1 + ... + c_m\alpha_m$, where the coefficients c_i are in the field K. However, every element of K can be written as a linear combination of the β's with coefficients in F, so each $c_i = d_{i1}\beta_1 + ... + d_{in}\beta_n$, where the d_{ij} are in F. Substituting these expressions for c_i, we get $\xi = (d_{11}\beta_1 + ... + d_{1n}\beta_n)\alpha_1 + ... + (d_{m1}\beta_1 + ... + d_{mn}\beta_n)\alpha_m = \sum d_{ij}\alpha_i\beta_j$, so that ξ has been expressed as a linear com-

FIELD EXTENSIONS

bination of the mn elements $\alpha_i\beta_j$ with coefficients in F. So these elements $\alpha_i\beta_j$ generate L, considered as a vector space over F.

Moreover, the elements $\alpha_i\beta_j$ are l.i. over F: suppose that $\sum d_{ij}\alpha_i\beta_j = 0$. Collecting the terms involving each α, we get $(d_{11}\beta_1 + \ldots + d_{1n}\beta_n)\alpha_1 + \ldots + (d_{m1}\beta_1 + \ldots + d_{mn}\beta_n)\alpha_m = 0$, and each coefficient here must be zero because the α's are l.i. over K. In other words $d_{11}\beta_1 + \ldots + d_{1n}\beta_n = 0, \ldots,$ $d_{m1}\beta_1 + \ldots + d_{mn}\beta_n = 0$. The fact that the β's are l.i. over F implies that each $d_{ij} = 0$. So the elements $\alpha_i\beta_j$ are l.i. as well as generating L, so they form a basis for L as a vector space over F. Thus the dimension is mn. That is to say, $[L:F] = [L:K][K:F]$.

Let F be a field and θ any complex number. If K is a field which contains F as a subfield and θ as an element, and L is another field containing F as a subfield and θ as an element, the intersection $L \cap K$ is a field (by Theorem 27) and will also have F as a subfield and θ as one of its elements. If now we take the intersection S of all fields containing F as a subfield and θ as an element, S is a field containing F and θ and has the property of being contained in any other such field:

DEFINITION. *The field S which is the intersection of all fields containing F as a subfield and θ as an element is denoted by $F(\theta)$, and is called the* **smallest field containing** F **and** θ. *Similarly, $F(\theta_1, \ldots, \theta_n)$ denotes the intersection of all fields containing F and the elements $\theta_1, \ldots, \theta_n$.*

Example 71. The set of all numbers $a + b\sqrt{2}$, where a, b are rational, is the smallest field containing **Q** and $\sqrt{2}$. So the notation used in Example 22 agrees with the last definition.

Example 72. The smallest field containing **R** and the element i is **C**. That is, $\mathbf{R}(i) = \mathbf{C}$.

Example 73. The number $\sqrt{3}$ does not belong to $\mathbf{Q}(\sqrt{2})$. Any field containing $\mathbf{Q}(\sqrt{2})$ and the element $\sqrt{3}$ must contain all numbers of the form $(a + b\sqrt{2}) + (c + d\sqrt{2})\sqrt{3}$, where a, b, c, d are in **Q**. This can be written $a + b\sqrt{2} + c\sqrt{3} + d\sqrt{6}$, and all numbers of this form do in fact form a field. It is easy to see that this set is closed under addition and multiplication, though not so easy to see that the inverse of such a number is also of the same form. So if we write $Q(\sqrt{2}) = K$, this set of numbers is $K(\sqrt{3})$.

Now $Q(\sqrt{3})$ consists of all numbers of the form $a + b\sqrt{3}$, where a, b are rational, and any field containing $Q(\sqrt{3})$ and $\sqrt{2}$ must contain all the numbers $(a + b\sqrt{3}) + (c + d\sqrt{3})\sqrt{2} = a + c\sqrt{2} + b\sqrt{3} + d\sqrt{6}$, which is the same set as before. If we put $Q(\sqrt{3}) = L$, then $L(\sqrt{2}) = K(\sqrt{3})$.

But any field containing Q and the elements $\sqrt{2}$ and $\sqrt{3}$ would have to contain also the product $\sqrt{2}\sqrt{3} = \sqrt{6}$, and thus all numbers $a + b\sqrt{2} + c\sqrt{3} + d\sqrt{6}$. Since these form a field, it is the smallest field containing Q and $\sqrt{2}$ and $\sqrt{3}$, which we denote by $Q(\sqrt{2},\sqrt{3})$. So $Q(\sqrt{2},\sqrt{3}) = K(\sqrt{3})$, and fairly clearly, $[K(\sqrt{3}):K] = 2$ and $[K:Q] = 2$, so, by Theorem 68, $[Q(\sqrt{2},\sqrt{3}):Q] = 4$. Alternatively, you can see that $1, \sqrt{2}, \sqrt{3}, \sqrt{6}$ form a basis for $Q(\sqrt{2},\sqrt{3})$ over Q.

Example 74. The field $Q(2^{1/3})$ consists of all numbers of the form $a + b2^{1/3} + c2^{2/3}$, where a, b, c are rational, and $[Q(2^{1/3}):Q] = 3$.

37. Roots of Polynomials

If $f(x)$ is a polynomial $a_0 + a_1x + ... + a_nx^n$, where the coefficients $a_0, ..., a_n$ are in C, and θ is any complex number, $f(\theta)$ denotes the number $a_0 + a_1\theta + ... + a_n\theta^n$. If $f(\theta) = 0$, we say that θ is a **root** of the polynomial $f(x)$. It is clear from the definition of addition and multiplication of polynomials that if $h(x) = f(x) + g(x)$, then $h(\theta) = f(\theta) + g(\theta)$, and if $h(x) = f(x)g(x)$, then $h(\theta) = f(\theta)g(\theta)$. These rules justify the familiar process of "putting $x = \theta$" in any equality of polynomials, as in the following theorem.

THEOREM 69 (**The Remainder Theorem**). *Given a polynomial $f(x)$ in $F[x]$, and a monic polynomial $x - \theta$ of degree one, then there is a polynomial $q(x)$ and a scalar r, such that $f(x) = (x - \theta)q(x) + r$, and $r = f(\theta)$.*

Proof. The existence of a unique quotient and remainder is given by the Division Algorithm. Since $x - \theta$ has degree one, the remainder is either zero or has degree zero, so is a scalar. Using the rules immediately preceding this theorem, we have $f(\theta) = (\theta - \theta)q(\theta) + r$, and so $r = f(\theta)$.

FIELD EXTENSIONS

THEOREM 70. *In $F[x]$, $x - \theta$ is a divisor of $f(x)$ if and only if $f(\theta) = 0$.*

Proof. If $x - \theta$ is a divisor of $f(x)$, $f(x) = (x - \theta)q(x)$ and so $f(\theta) = (\theta - \theta)q(\theta) = 0$. Conversely, from the Remainder Theorem, $f(x) = (x - \theta)q(x) + f(\theta)$, and so if $f(\theta) = 0$, then $f(x) = (x - \theta)q(x)$.

38. Simple Algebraic Extensions

DEFINITION. *The complex number θ is* **algebraic** *over the field F if it is a root of a polynomial with coefficients, not all zero, in F. Otherwise θ is* **transcendental** *over F.*

Example 75. Any complex number is algebraic over **R**.

Example 76. The number $\sqrt{2}$ is algebraic over **Q**, since it is the root of $x^2 - 2$, which has rational coefficients. Similarly, i is algebraic over **Q**, since i is a root of $x^2 + 1$. The number $\sqrt{(2 + \sqrt{3})}$, for example, is algebraic over **Q**. For if $\theta = \sqrt{(2 + \sqrt{3})}$, then $\theta^2 = 2 + \sqrt{3}$, so $(\theta^2 - 2)^2 = 3$. Therefore, $\theta^4 - 4\theta^2 + 1 = 0$. So θ is a root of $x^4 - 4x^2 + 1$, which is a polynomial with rational coefficients.

Example 77. It is well-known, but not easily shown, that π and e are transcendental over **Q**.

If θ is algebraic over F, the extension $F(\theta)$ is called a **simple algebraic** extension of F, and our aim now is to show that any simple algebraic extension is a finite extension.

DEFINITION. *If θ is algebraic over F, the* **minimum polynomial** $m(x)$ *for θ over F, is the monic polynomial, with coefficients in F, of smallest degree, with θ as a root. If $m(x)$ has degree n, then θ is algebraic over F* **of degree** *n.*

THEOREM 71.

(i) *The minimum polynomial is irreducible.*

(ii) *Any polynomial with θ as a root is a multiple of the minimum polynomial for θ.*

Proof. (i) If $m(x) = f(x)g(x)$, then $f(\theta)g(\theta) = m(\theta) = 0$. This implies that either $f(\theta) = 0$ or $g(\theta) = 0$. If either $f(x)$ or $g(x)$

had degree less than $m(x)$, θ would be the root of a polynomial of smaller degree than $m(x)$. Therefore $m(x)$ is irreducible.

(ii) If θ is a root of $f(x)$, write $f(x) = m(x)q(x) + r(x)$, where either $r(x) = 0$ or deg $r(x) <$ deg $m(x)$. Then $f(\theta) = m(\theta)q(\theta) + r(\theta)$. Since $f(\theta) = 0$ and $m(\theta) = 0$, we have $r(\theta) = 0$. So, if $r(x) \neq 0$, it is a polynomial of smaller degree than $m(x)$ with θ as a root, which is a contradiction. Therefore $r(x) = 0$, and $f(x)$ is a multiple of $m(x)$.

THEOREM 72. *If θ is algebraic over F, then $F(\theta)$ consists of those numbers that can be written in the form $f(\theta)$, where $f(x)$ is a polynomial over F.*

Proof. Let H be the set of all numbers that can be written as $f(\theta)$, where $f(x)$ is a polynomial over F. We can show that H is a field:

H is closed under addition and multiplication, contains 0 and 1, and contains, with every element, also its negative. We must show that H contains, with every non-zero element $f(\theta)$, also its inverse. If $f(\theta) \neq 0$, θ is not a root of $f(x)$, so $m(x)$ does not divide $f(x)$. It follows that $m(x)$ and $f(x)$ have h.c.f. 1, since $m(x)$ is irreducible. Therefore there are polynomials $s(x)$ and $t(x)$ such that $s(x)m(x) + t(x)f(x) = 1$. Substituting θ for x, we get $s(\theta)m(\theta) + t(\theta)f(\theta) = 1$, and, since $m(\theta) = 0$, $t(\theta)f(\theta) = 1$. Thus the number $t(\theta)$, which is an element of H, is an inverse for the given element $f(\theta)$. So H is a field.

Now, any field containing F and θ must contain 1 and all the positive integer powers of θ and hence any finite linear combination of these (with coefficients in F). That is to say, any field containing F and θ must contain all the numbers in H. So $F(\theta) \supseteq H$. But $F(\theta)$ is contained in any field containing F and θ, so $F(\theta) \subseteq H$. Therefore $F(\theta) = H$, i.e. $F(\theta)$ consists of those numbers that can be written in the given form.

THEOREM 73. *If θ is algebraic over F of degree n, any element of $F(\theta)$ can be written as $f(\theta)$, where $f(x)$ is a polynomial over F,*

FIELD EXTENSIONS

of degree at most $n - 1$. $F(\theta)$ is a finite extension of F, and $[F(\theta):F] = n$.

Proof. Any element of $F(\theta)$ is $f(\theta)$, where $f(x)$ is a polynomial over F. But $f(x) = m(x)q(x) + r(x)$, where either $r(x) = 0$ or $\deg r(x) < \deg m(x)$. Then $f(\theta) = r(\theta)$, since $m(\theta) = 0$. So the element expressed as $f(\theta)$ can be expressed as $r(\theta)$ instead, where now $r(x)$ has degree at most $n - 1$.

This means that, considered as a vector space over F, $F(\theta)$ is generated by $1, \theta, \theta^2, ..., \theta^{n-1}$. But, in addition, these are l.i. over F, for if $c_0 1 + c_1\theta + c_2\theta^2 + ... + c_{n-1}\theta^{n-1} = 0$, with the c's not all zero, then θ is a root of a polynomial of smaller degree than the minimum polynomial. Therefore $1, \theta, \theta^2, ..., \theta^{n-1}$ is a basis for $F(\theta)$ over F. Hence $[F(\theta):F] = n$.

Example 78. The number $\theta = \sqrt{(2 + \sqrt{3})}$ is a root of $x^4 - 4x^2 + 1$ (see Example 76). This polynomial is irreducible over $\mathbf{Q}$. For the only possible linear factors with integer coefficients are $x \pm 1$, and you can show that these are not factors using, say, Theorem 70. The polynomial could factorise into $(x^2 + ax + 1)(x^2 + bx + 1)$ or $(x^2 + ax - 1)(x^2 + bx - 1)$, but it is an easy matter to show that there are no integers a, b which are correct. Since the polynomial has no factors with integer coefficients, it is irreducible over $\mathbf{Q}$, using the result of p. 51. Therefore $x^4 - 4x^2 + 1$ is the minimum polynomial for $\theta = \sqrt{(2 + \sqrt{3})}$, and so $[\mathbf{Q}(\theta):\mathbf{Q}] = 4$, and $\mathbf{Q}(\theta)$ consists of all numbers $a + b\theta + c\theta^2 + d\theta^3$, where a, b, c, d are rational.

THEOREM 74.

(i) *If K is a finite extension of F of degree n, then any element of K is algebraic over F of degree m, where $m \mid n$.*

(ii) *If K is a finite extension of F of degree 2^m, and α is algebraic over F of degree 3, then α is not in K.*

Proof. If α is in K, then $1, \alpha, \alpha^2, ..., \alpha^n$ are l.d. over F, because considering K as a vector space over F, they are a set of $n + 1$ elements in a vector space of dimension n (see Theorem 67(ii)). Hence there are scalars (elements of F), not all zero, such that $c_0 1 + c_1\alpha + ... + c_n\alpha^n = 0$. Therefore α is a root of a polynomial over F (of degree at most n), and so α is algebraic over F.

64

A MORE SOPHISTICATED APPROACH

Now the field $F(\alpha)$ is such that $K \supseteq F(\alpha) \supseteq F$. If α is algebraic over F of degree m, then $F(\alpha)$ is a finite extension of F with $[F(\alpha):F] = m$. Moreover, K is a finite extension of F and hence of $F(\alpha)$, so, by Theorem 68, $[K:F] = [K:F(\alpha)][F(\alpha):F]$. Here $[F(\alpha):F] = m$ and $[K:F] = n$, so $m \mid n$.

(ii) This follows from (i) because 3 does not divide 2^m, and is inserted here explicitly, because we shall want to use it when we consider constructions with ruler and compasses.

39. A More Sophisticated Approach

The theory of algebraic extensions can be described very neatly using the concepts of homomorphism and maximal ideals: If θ is algebraic over F, define a mapping ϕ from the ring $F[x]$ of polynomials over F into the field $F(\theta)$, by $\phi(f(x)) = f(\theta)$. We have seen that the simple substitution of θ for x satisfies the properties that if $h(x) = f(x) + g(x)$ then $h(\theta) = f(\theta) + g(\theta)$, and if $h(x) = f(x)g(x)$ then $h(\theta) = f(\theta)g(\theta)$. This shows that $\phi: F[x] \to F(\theta)$ is a homomorphism. Now the kernel is the set of those polynomials $f(x)$ such that $\phi(f(x)) = 0$, i.e. such that $f(\theta) = 0$. By Theorem 71(ii), this is the principal ideal generated by the minimum polynomial $m(x)$. By Theorem 47, Im ϕ is isomorphic to the quotient ring $F[x]/(m(x))$. But since $m(x)$ is irreducible, $(m(x))$ is maximal and so $F[x]/(m(x))$ is a field. Hence Im ϕ is a subfield of $F(\theta)$. But θ belongs to Im ϕ because $\theta = \phi(x)$, and if a is any element of F, a is in Im ϕ because $a = \phi(a)$. Therefore Im ϕ is a field containing θ and all the elements of F, so Im ϕ is the whole of $F(\theta)$. Thus $F(\theta)$ is isomorphic to $F[x]/(m(x))$.

If θ is transcendental over F, we may again define a mapping $\phi: F[x] \to F(\theta)$. In this case the kernel is $\{0\}$ since there is no polynomial $f(x)$ such that $f(\theta) = 0$. We cannot, however, prove that Im $\phi = F(\theta)$, so when θ is transcendental over F, the extension $F(\theta)$ has a subring which is isomorphic to the polynomial ring $F[x]$. In fact, the extension $F(\theta)$ is isomorphic to the field $F(x)$ of all rational functions over F (see Example 26).

40. Constructions with Ruler and Compasses

The ideas just developed can be used to discover whether certain geometrical constructions with ruler and compasses are possible. By "ruler" we mean just a "straight-edge", which enables us to draw a line through two given points. With the compasses, we can draw a circle if we are given its centre and radius.

We assume that in the plane we have some fixed Cartesian coordinate axes, with a unit length given, so that every point in the plane has coordinates (x, y), where x, y are real numbers. Starting with, in effect, the two given points $O = (0, 0)$ and $A = (1, 0)$, which fix the unit length, it is not difficult to show that any point with rational coordinates can be constructed with ruler and compasses (when we talk about constructions in future, we shall assume that "with ruler and compasses" is understood): All points with integer coordinates are easily constructed. Then for any integers m, n the point $(m/n, 0)$ can be constructed as follows. Let M be the point $(0, m)$ and N be $(0, n)$. The line through M parallel to NA, which can be drawn by a well-known elementary geometrical construction, meets OA in the required point. From this, any point with rational coordinates can be constructed.

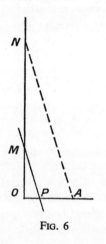

FIG. 6

Now suppose, instead, that a certain set of points in the

plane is given. What can we say about the points which can be constructed from these? The answer is that if F is the smallest field containing the coordinates of the given points, then any point that can be constructed from them has coordinates belonging to an extension of F of degree a power of 2:

THEOREM 75. *Let F be the smallest field containing all the coordinates of a given set of points in the plane. If P is a point that can be constructed from the given points by a finite number of constructions with ruler and compasses, the coordinates of P belong to an extension K of F, where $[K:F] = 2^m$ and m is an integer ≥ 0.*

Proof. A single construction with ruler and compasses is of one of three types. A new point P is constructed from given points A, B, C, D which are already given, where either

   (i) P is the intersection of two lines,

   (ii) P is the intersection of a line and a circle,

or (iii) P is the intersection of two circles.

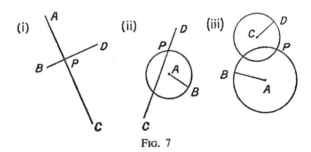

FIG. 7

Suppose that the coordinates of A, B, C, D belong to a field F. In case (i), the equations of AC and BD are linear with coefficients in F. So the coordinates of P, which are found by solving the two simultaneous linear equations, are also in F. In case (ii), the equation of CD is linear and the equation of the circle, centre A, radius AB, is $x^2 + y^2 + 2gx + 2fy + c = 0$, where g, f, c are in F. The x-coordinate of P is then the root of a quadratic equation with coefficients in F, and the y-coordinate is obtained from the x-coordinate by the linear equation. Thus the coordinates of P belong to an extension of F of degree 2 or to F itself, depending on whether the quadratic equation is irreducible or not. In case (iii), the equations of the two circles are $x^2 + y^2 + 2gx + 2fy + c = 0$ and $x^2 + y^2 + 2g'x + 2f'y + c' = 0$. The solution of these two equations is the same as the solution of either circle and the line $2(g - g')x + 2(f - f')y + (c - c') = 0$, which is the case dealt with in (ii.)

Now, the coordinates of the given points belong to the field $F = F_0$, say. Suppose that P is constructed by k constructions. Let F_i be the smallest field containing the coordinates of all the points so far obtained after i constructions, for $i = 1, 2, ..., k$. We have shown that either $F_i = F_{i-1}$ or F_i is an extension of F_{i-1} of degree 2. Thus for each i, $[F_i : F_{i-1}] = 1$ or 2. Therefore $[F_k : F_0] = [F_k : F_{k-1}] [F_{k-1} : F_{k-2}] ... [F_1 : F_0] = 2^m$, where $0 \le m \le k$. Hence the coordinates of P belong to F_k which is an extension of F of degree 2^m.

THEOREM 76 (**The Impossibility of Trisecting an Angle in General**). *Given two lines OA and OB intersecting at O, there is no general method of constructing a line OC such that* $\angle AOB = 3 \angle AOC$.

Proof. To show that there is no general method, it is sufficient to give one angle that cannot be trisected and it is convenient to choose an angle of 60°.

Choose A and B on the unit circle, centre O, with OA as the x-axis, so that O, A, B are (0, 0), (1, 0), (cos 60°, sin 60°). These belong to $\mathbf{Q}(\sqrt{3})$. Trisection of the angle is equivalent to the construction of a point $C = (\cos 20°, \sin 20°)$. Now $\cos 3\theta = 4 \cos^3\theta - 3 \cos \theta$, so $8 \cos^3 20° - 6 \cos 20° = 2 \cos 60° = 1$. Thus cos 20° is a root of $8x^3 - 6x - 1$, which is irreducible over $\mathbf{Q}$ (see Example 59). Thus cos 20° is algebraic over $\mathbf{Q}$ of degree 3. By Theorem 74 (ii), cos 20° does not belong to

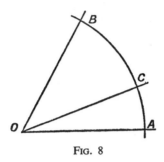

FIG. 8

any extension of $\mathbf{Q}$ of degree 2^m, whereas any constructible point has coordinates belonging to an extension of $\mathbf{Q}(\sqrt{3})$ of degree a power of 2, which would be an extension of $\mathbf{Q}$ of degree a power of 2. Thus C cannot be obtained by a finite number of ruler-and-compasses constructions.

Example 79. It is impossible to construct a regular 7-sided polygon with ruler and compasses. This would be equivalent to the construction of the point (cos $2\pi/7$, sin $2\pi/7$) from the points $O = (0, 0)$, $A = (1, 0)$. If we write $\epsilon = \exp(2\pi i/7)$, then ϵ is a root of $x^7 - 1$.
Since $x^7 - 1 = (x - 1)(x^6 + x^5 + x^4 + x^3 + x^2 + x + 1)$,
we have $\epsilon^6 + \epsilon^5 + \epsilon^4 + \epsilon^3 + \epsilon^2 + \epsilon + 1 = 0$,
or $\epsilon^3 + \epsilon^2 + \epsilon + 1 + \epsilon^{-1} + \epsilon^{-2} + \epsilon^{-3} = 0$.
But $\epsilon = \cos 2\pi/7 + i \sin 2\pi/7$ and $\epsilon^{-1} = \cos 2\pi/7 - i \sin 2\pi/7$, so $\epsilon + \epsilon^{-1} = 2c$, where $c = \cos 2\pi/7$. Squaring and cubing, we get $\epsilon^2 + \epsilon^{-2} + 2 =$ and $4c^2$ and $\epsilon^3 + \epsilon^{-3} + 3(\epsilon + \epsilon^{-1}) = 8c^3$. Thus $\epsilon^2 + \epsilon^{-2} = 4c^2 - 2$, $\epsilon^3 + \epsilon^{-3} = 8c^3 - 6c$. Hence $(8c^3 - 6c) + (4c^2 - 2) + 2c + 1 = 0$, or $8c^3 + 4c^2 - 4c - 1 = 0$. Thus $2c$ is a root of the irreducible polynomial $x^3 + x^2 - 2x - 1$, (see Exercise 18, Chapter 6). Therefore cos $2\pi/7$ is also the root of an irreducible cubic polynomial and, combining Theorems 74(ii) and 75 again, the construction of the regular 7-sided polygon is impossible.

Exercises for this chapter will be found on p. 76.

Exercises

CHAPTER ONE

1. Which of the following sets are integral domains?
   (i) The set of all even integers,
   (ii) The set of all odd integers,
   (iii) The set of all rational numbers whose denominators are 1 or a power of 2,
   (iv) The set of all real numbers of the form $a + b\sqrt{3}$, where a and b are integers.

2. Show that the set of 2×2 matrices of the form $\begin{pmatrix} a & b \\ b & a \end{pmatrix}$, where a and b are in J_2, consists of 4 matrices and is closed under addition and multiplication. Denoting the matrices by $\mathbf{O}, \mathbf{I}, \mathbf{A}, \mathbf{B}$ in an appropriate way, give the addition and multiplication tables. Which of the postulates **1** to **9** for an integral domain are satisfied?

3. Prove that the following rules hold in any integral domain, justifying each step by a postulate, a result established in the text, or an earlier exercise:
   (i) If $a + b = a + c$, then $b = c$.
   (ii) If $a + b = a$, then $b = 0$.
   (iii) $-(a + b) = (-a) + (-b)$.
   (iv) $-(a - b) = b - a$.
   (v) $a(b - c) = ab - ac$.

4. Show that in an integral domain, the only elements satisfying $x^2 = x$ are 0 and 1.

5. Give the addition and multiplication tables for J_5. In J_5, solve the equation $2x = 3$.

6. Show that every non-zero element of J_5 satisfies $x^4 = 1$, and hence that every element of J_5 satisfies $x^5 = x$.

7. Give the addition and multiplication tables for J_6. In J_6, find all the solutions of the equations:
   (i) $4x = 2$, (ii) $4x = 3$, (iii) $x^2 + 2x + 3 = 0$, (iv) $x^2 + 2x + 5 = 0$.

8. Find all the divisors of zero in J_{10} and J_{12}.

CHAPTER TWO

1. Prove that the following rules hold in any ordered integral domain:
   (i) $a - b < a - c$ if and only if $b > c$.
   (ii) If $a < b$ and $c < 0$, then $ac > bc$.
   (iii) If $a < b$, then $-a > -b$.

EXERCISES

2. Show that, in an ordered integral domain, the sum and the product of any finite number of positive elements are positive.

3. Show that, in an ordered integral domain, the postulate **9**, that there are no divisors of zero, can be deduced from the other postulates (namely **1** to **8** and **P1, P2, P3**).

4. Let D be an integral domain on which there is a transitive relation $<$ satisfying **O1, O2, O3**, and define a to be positive if $0 < a$. Prove that **P1, P2, P3** hold and that therefore D is ordered.

5. Show that for any elements a and b in a well-ordered integral domain, $|ab| \geqslant |a|$.

6. Prove that in a well-ordered integral domain, $a - 1$ is the greatest element less than a.

CHAPTER THREE

1. Show the validity of the following principle of induction:
Let there be associated with each integer $n \geqslant a$, where a is a positive integer, a proposition $P(n)$ which is either true or false. If $P(a)$ is true, and for all $k \geqslant a$, $P(k)$ implies $P(k + 1)$, then $P(n)$ is true for all integers $n \geqslant a$.

2. Show that if a is positive and not a prime, then it has a divisor $\leqslant \sqrt{a}$.

3. Write down all the primes less than 100.

4. Write down all pairs of relatively prime positive integers less than 10.

5. Show that if there are integers s and t such that $sa + tb = 1$, then a and b are relatively prime.

6. Show that if $(a, c) = (b, c) = 1$, then $(ab, c) = 1$.

7. Show that if $(a, b) = 1$ and $a \mid c$ and $b \mid c$, then $ab \mid c$.

8. Show that if $(a, b) = d$ and $a \mid c$ and $b \mid c$, then $ab \mid cd$.

9. Show that $(a, (b, c)) = (b, (c, a)) = (c, (a, b))$.

10. If m, n are relatively prime positive integers, and a, b are any integers, show that there is an integer x such that $x \equiv a \pmod{m}$ and $x \equiv b \pmod{n}$. [Hint: Consider the remainders of a, $a + m$, $a + 2m$, ..., $a + (n - 1)m$, on division by n.]

11. Find the h.c.f. of each pair of integers, and express it in the form $sa + tb$:
(i) $a = 323$, $b = 209$, (ii) $a = 1701$, $b = 672$.

12. If the positive integer $n = p^\alpha q^\beta$, where p, q are different primes, show that integers s and t can be found so that $1/n = s/p^\alpha + t/q^\beta$. Find s and t such that $1/225 = s/9 + t/25$.

13. The least common multiple of two integers a, b, denoted by $[a, b]$, is the positive integer d such that $a \mid d$ and $b \mid d$ and, whenever $a \mid x$ and $b \mid x$ then $d \mid x$. Show that $[a, b]$ divides ab, and that $ab/[a, b] = \pm (a, b)$.

71

F

14. If $a = p_1^{\alpha_1} p_2^{\alpha_2} \ldots p_r^{\alpha_r}$ and $b = p_1^{\beta_1} p_2^{\beta_2} \ldots p_r^{\beta_r}$, where $p_1, \ldots, p_r$ are distinct primes and each $\alpha_i \geqslant 0$ and $\beta_i \geqslant 0$, prove that $(a, b) = p_1^{\gamma_1} p_2^{\gamma_2} \ldots p_r^{\gamma_r}$ and $[a, b] = p_1^{\delta_1} p_2^{\delta_2} \ldots p_r^{\delta_r}$, where, for each i, γ_i is the minimum and δ_i is the maximum of α_i and β_i.

CHAPTER FOUR

1. Show that the set $Q(\sqrt{3})$ of all real numbers of the form $a + b\sqrt{3}$, where a, b are rational, forms a field.

2. Show that Q has no proper subfields.

3. Show that Q is the only proper subfield of $Q(\sqrt{2})$.

4. Show that $Q(\sqrt{2}) \cap Q(\sqrt{3}) = Q$.

5. Show that the set of all real numbers $a + b\sqrt{2} + c\sqrt{3}$, where a, b, c are rational, is not a field; but that the set of all real numbers $a + b\sqrt{2} + c\sqrt{3} + d\sqrt{6}$, where a, b, c, d are rational, *is* a field.

6. Let S be the set of ordered pairs (a, b), where a, b are real numbers and we say $(a, b) = (c, d)$ if and only if $a = c$ and $b = d$. (The notation here does not stand for h.c.f.). Show that the elements of S, with addition and multiplication defined by

$$(a, b) + (c, d) = (a + c, b + d),$$
$$(a, b)(c, d) = (ac - bd, bc + ad),$$

form a field.

7. Show that the numbers 0, 2, 4, 6, 8 with addition and multiplication modulo 10 form a field in which 6 is the identity element.

8. Show that, in Theorem 26, (ii) can be replaced by (ii)' S contains at least two elements.

9. Prove that any field of characteristic p has a subfield of p elements.

10. Show that if the sum $1 + 1 + \ldots + 1$ (k times) $= 0$ in a field of characteristic p, then k is a multiple of p.

11. If a finite field of characteristic p has q elements, prove that q is a multiple of p. (Actually $q = p^n$, for some n, see Exercise 11, Chapter 8.)

CHAPTER FIVE

1. If a, b, c, d are elements of a ring, expand $(a + b)(c + d)$. Show that $(a + b)^2 = a^2 + ab + ba + b^2$.

2. If every element of a ring R satisfies $x^2 = x$, prove that R is commutative.

EXERCISES

3. Show that the set of all 2×2 matrices $\begin{pmatrix} p & q \\ r & s \end{pmatrix}$, where p, q, r, s are *integers*, form a subring of the ring of all 2×2 real matrices.

4. Let S be the set of ordered pairs (a, b), where a, b are integers, with addition and multiplication defined by

$$(a, b) + (c, d) = (a + c, b + d),$$
$$(a, b)(c, d) = (ac, bd).$$

Prove that S is a commutative ring with identity. Show that S is not an integral domain.

5. The operations $\oplus$ and $\otimes$ are defined on the set of integers by

$$a \oplus b = a + b + 1,$$
$$a \otimes b = a + b + ab,$$

where the addition and multiplication on the right hand side are the usual operations in $\mathbf{J}$. Show that the integers, with $\oplus$ as addition and $\otimes$ as multiplication, form a ring $\mathbf{J}'$. What are the zero and identity of $\mathbf{J}'$?

6. Show that any proper ideal of $\mathbf{J}[i]$ contains some positive integer.

7. Find all the ideals U of $\mathbf{J}_{12}$. In each case, describe $\mathbf{J}_{12}/U$ by finding a familiar ring with which the quotient ring is isomorphic.

8. Show that the multiples of 8 (i.e. the integers $\dots, -16, -8, 0, 8, 16, \dots$) form an ideal in the ring R of even integers. Give the addition and multiplication tables for R/U. Is this quotient ring isomorphic to $\mathbf{J}_4$?

9. Find all the maximal ideals in $\mathbf{J}_{12}$.

10. Let R be a commutative ring with identity. An ideal U is **prime** if for all a, b in R, ab is in U only if a is in U or b is in U. Prove that U is a prime ideal if and only if R/U is an integral domain. Show that every maximal ideal is prime.

11. Let S be the ring of Exercise 4. Show that
   (i) the set of all pairs (a, b), with a even, is a maximal ideal,
   (ii) the set of all pairs $(a, 0)$ is a prime ideal which is not maximal,
   (iii) the set of all pairs $(a, 0)$, where a is a multiple of 4, is an ideal which is not prime.

12. Show that the mapping ϕ from $\mathbf{R}$ into the set of 2×2 real matrices, defined by $\phi(a) = \begin{pmatrix} a & 0 \\ 0 & a \end{pmatrix}$, is a monomorphism.

13. Show that the mapping ϕ from $\mathbf{C}$ into the set of 2×2 real matrices, defined by $\phi(a + bi) = \begin{pmatrix} a & b \\ -b & a \end{pmatrix}$, is a monomorphism.

14. Is the mapping $\phi: \mathbf{J}[\sqrt{2}] \to \mathbf{J}[\sqrt{3}]$, defined by $\phi(a + b\sqrt{2}) = a + b\sqrt{3}$, a homomorphism?

73

EXERCISES

15. If R, R' are commutative rings with identities and $\phi: R \to R'$ is a homomorphism, show that it is not necessarily the case that $\phi(1) = 1$. Prove that if ϕ is an epimorphism, then $\phi(1)$ *is* the identity element of R'.

16. Show that the ring $\mathbf{J}'$ of Exercise 5 is isomorphic to $\mathbf{J}$.

17. Prove that the field of Exercise 7, Chapter 4, is isomorphic to $\mathbf{J}_5$, and give the isomorphism explicitly.

18. If D, D' are ordered integral domains, the isomorphism $\phi: D \to D'$ is called an **order-isomorphism** if, for all elements a and b in D, $a < b$ implies $\phi(a) < \phi(b)$. Show that in any ordered integral domain, the elements $\ldots, -(1 + 1), -1, 0, 1, 1 + 1, \ldots$ form a subdomain order-isomorphic to the integers. Furthermore, using Theorems 12 and 13, show that any *well*-ordered integral domain is order-isomorphic to the domain of integers. (This clarifies the language of p. 15).

CHAPTER SIX

1. Show that if R is a ring, the set of polynomials $R[x]$ over R can be defined, and prove that $R[x]$ is a ring. Show that Theorem 48 holds if and only if R is an integral domain.

2. In *any* commutative ring with identity, a is called a unit if there is an element b such that $ab = 1$. Show that a unit cannot be a divisor of zero. Find the units in $\mathbf{J}_6$, $\mathbf{J}_7$, $\mathbf{J}_8$.

3. (i) Show that the relation of being associates is an equivalence relation.

(ii) Show that the associates of 1 are the units.

(iii) If a is an associate of b, show that $a \mid c$ implies $b \mid c$, and $c \mid a$ implies $c \mid b$.

4. Show that if a Gaussian integer is neither real nor pure imaginary, its four associates lie in the four quadrants of the Argand diagram.

5. In $\mathbf{J}[i]$, find a h.c.f. of $1 + 5i$ and $4 + 2i$.

6. In $\mathbf{J}[i]$, define, as in the text, $\nu(a + bi) = a^2 + b^2$. Show that
   (i) if $x \mid y$, then $\nu(x) \mid \nu(y)$,
   (ii) x is a unit if and only if $\nu(x) = 1$,
   (iii) x is irreducible if and only if $\nu(x)$ is prime.
Factorise each of the following into a product of irreducible elements: $4 + 3i, 5, 1 + 3i$.

7. In $\mathbf{J}[\sqrt{2}]$, define $\nu(a + b\sqrt{2}) = |a^2 - 2b^2|$. Show that
   (i) $\nu(xy) = \nu(x) \cdot \nu(y)$,
   (ii) x is a unit if and only if $\nu(x) = 1$,
   (iii) x is irreducible if and only if $\nu(x)$ is prime.
Factorise each of the following into a product of irreducible elements: $4 + \sqrt{2}, 2, 1 + 2\sqrt{2}$.

EXERCISES

8. In the set $J[\sqrt{(-5)}]$ of all complex numbers of the form $a + b\sqrt{(-5)}$, define $\nu(a + b\sqrt{(-5)}) = a^2 + 5b^2$. Show that

(i) $\nu(xy) = \nu(x) \cdot \nu(y)$,

(ii) the units are ± 1.

Show that 3, 7, $1 + 2\sqrt{(-5)}$, $1 - 2\sqrt{(-5)}$ are all irreducible elements and deduce that 21 can be factorised into a product of irreducible elements in two distinct ways. Prove that 14 also has two distinct factorisations.

9. In a Euclidean ring, show that if d is an h.c.f. of a and b, then any associate of d is also an h.c.f. of a and b.

10. If $a(x) = x^4 + 2x^3 + x^2 + 4x + 1$ and $b(x) = x^2 + x + 1$, find real polynomials $q(x)$, $r(x)$ such that $a(x) = b(x)q(x) + r(x)$, where deg $r(x) <$ deg $b(x)$, by the method outlined in the proof of Theorem 52. Compare the working with the familiar method of long division of polynomials.

11. In $\mathbf{R}[x]$, find the h.c.f. of $a(x) = x^4 - x^3 - x + 1$ and $b(x) = x^4 - 2x^3 + 2x - 1$, and express it in the form $s(x)a(x) + t(x)b(x)$ using Euclid's Algorithm.

12. In $\mathbf{C}[x]$, find the h.c.f. of the polynomials $x^3 - 2ix^2 + ix + 2$ and $x^2 + (1 - 2i)x - 2i$.

13. Factorise each of the following into a product of irreducible polynomials: (i) $x^4 + 4$, in $J_5[x]$, (ii) $x^2 + 3$, in $J_7[x]$, (iii) $x^2 + 1$, in $J_7[x]$, (iv) $x^3 + 2$, in $J_{11}[x]$.

14. Find all the irreducible polynomials of degree 2 or 3 in $J_2[x]$.

15. Show that, in $F[x]$, any polynomial can be written as a scalar times a product of irreducible monic polynomials, where the scalar is unique and the irreducible polynomials are unique apart from the order in which they occur.

16. Express each of the following as the product of its content and a primitive polynomial: $3x^2 - 15x + 6$, $-x^2 - 2x - 1$, $x^2 - 3x/4 + 1/2$, $-9x^2/2 - 15x/2 + 3$.

17. If θ is rational, and $x - \theta$ divides a monic polynomial with integer coefficients, prove that θ is an integer.

18. Show that $x^3 + x^2 - 2x - 1$ is irreducible over $\mathbf{Q}$.

CHAPTER SEVEN

1. Prove that the set of all 2×2 real matrices is a vector space over $\mathbf{R}$, where addition is defined as usual and multiplication by scalars is defined by $c\begin{pmatrix} p & q \\ r & s \end{pmatrix} = \begin{pmatrix} cp & cq \\ cr & cs \end{pmatrix}$.

Show that $\begin{pmatrix} 1 & 0 \\ 0 & 0 \end{pmatrix}$, $\begin{pmatrix} 0 & 1 \\ 0 & 0 \end{pmatrix}$, $\begin{pmatrix} 0 & 0 \\ 1 & 0 \end{pmatrix}$, $\begin{pmatrix} 0 & 0 \\ 0 & 1 \end{pmatrix}$ form a basis.

EXERCISES

2. Show that 2 elements of a vector space are l.d. if and only if one is a multiple of the other.

3. Find whether the following sets are l.d. or l.i.
 (i) $(12, 6, 0), (3, -2, 1), (1, 4, -1)$ in $V_3(\mathbf{R})$.
 (ii) $(1, 2, -1, 0), (-3, 0, 1, 2), (2, 1, 0, -1)$ in $V_4(\mathbf{R})$.
 (iii) $x^2 + 3x + 4, x^2 + 2x + 1, 4x + 2$ in $\mathbf{Q}[x]$.
 (iv) $x^2 + 3x + 4, x^2 + 2x + 1, 4x + 2$ in $J_5[x]$.

4. Show that $(0, 1, 1), (1, 0, 1), (1, 1, 0)$ are l.i. in $V_3(\mathbf{R})$. For what fields F would they be l.d. considered as elements of $V_3(F)$?

5. Show that $(9, -15, -6, 24), (-15, 25, 10, -40), (16, 12, 15, -10)$ are l.d. in $V_4(\mathbf{R})$, but that the third is not a linear combination of the first two.

6. Show that, in $V_n(F)$, the coordinates of $\mathbf{x} = (x_1, ..., x_n)$ with respect to the natural basis $\mathbf{e}_1, ..., \mathbf{e}_n$ are $x_1, ..., x_n$.

7. Show that $(2, 1, 1), (-2, 1, 3)$ and $(3, 1, -1)$ form a basis for $V_3(\mathbf{R})$. Find the coordinates of $(2, 1, 0)$ and $(-1, 1, 1)$ with respect to this basis.

8. Show that $(1, 1, 0, 0), (0, 0, 1, 1), (1, 0, 0, 4), (0, 0, 0, 2)$ form a basis for $V_4(\mathbf{R})$. Find the coordinates of $\mathbf{e}_1, \mathbf{e}_2, \mathbf{e}_3, \mathbf{e}_4$ with respect to this basis.

9. If, in a vector space, ξ has coordinates $x_1, ..., x_n$ and η has coordinates $y_1, ..., y_n$ with respect to some basis, prove that $\xi + \eta$ has coordinates $x_1+y_1, ..., x_n+y_n$ and $c\xi$ has coordinates $cx_1, ..., cx_n$.

10. A mapping $\phi: V \to V'$, where V, V' are vector spaces over the same field F, is called a **homomorphism** (or **linear transformation**) if $\phi(\xi + \eta) = \phi(\xi) + \phi(\eta)$, and $\phi(c\xi) = c.\phi(\xi)$, for all ξ, η in V, c in F. Define, by analogy with homomorphisms of rings, Ker ϕ and Im ϕ, and hence an isomorphism.

Let $\alpha_1, ..., \alpha_n$ be a basis for a vector space V over a field F. Prove that the mapping $\phi: V \to V_n(F)$, defined by $\phi(\xi) = (x_1, ..., x_n)$, where $x_1, ..., x_n$ are the coordinates of ξ with respect to $\alpha_1, ..., \alpha_n$ as basis, is an isomorphism.

CHAPTER EIGHT

1. Show that (i) $[K:F] = 1$ if and only if $K = F$, (ii) $[F(\theta):F] = 1$ if and only if θ belongs to F.

2. Show that each of the following is algebraic over $\mathbf{Q}$:
 $1 + 2\sqrt{2}, \sqrt{2} + \sqrt{5}, 2 + i, \sqrt{(1 + 2^{2/3})}, (i + \sqrt{2})^{1/3}$.

3. Find the minimum polynomial over $\mathbf{Q}$ of each of the following:
$i + \sqrt{3}, \sqrt{(5 - \sqrt{2})}, \sqrt{(\frac{1}{2} + \sqrt{5})}$.

4. Prove that $\mathbf{Q}(\sqrt{2}, 2^{1/3})$ is an extension of $\mathbf{Q}$ of degree 6, and that $1, 2^{1/6}, 2^{1/3}, 2^{1/2}, 2^{2/3}, 2^{5/6}$ is a basis. Deduce that $\mathbf{Q}(\sqrt{2}, 2^{1/3}) = \mathbf{Q}(2^{1/6})$.

5. If $\theta = \sqrt{(2 + \sqrt{3})}$, show that $1, \theta, \sqrt{3}, \theta\sqrt{3}$ form a basis for $\mathbf{Q}(\theta)$ over $\mathbf{Q}$.

6. If θ_1, θ_2 are algebraic over F of degrees m, n, where m, n are relatively prime, prove that $[F(\theta_1, \theta_2): F] = mn$.

7. If θ is a root of $x^3 + 5x + 1$, use the method of Theorem 72 to express $(\theta^2 - \theta + 1)^{-1}$ in the form $a + b\theta + c\theta^2$, where a, b, c are rational.

8. Express $(1 + 2^{1/3})^{-1}$ as $f(2^{1/3})$, where $f(x)$ is a polynomial over $\mathbf{Q}$ of degree 2.

9. Prove that a polynomial over F of degree n has at most n distinct roots in F. [Hint: use Theorem 70 and induction on n.]

10. Prove that a polynomial of degree 2 or 3 is irreducible over F if and only if it has no roots in F.

11. Let K be a finite field of characteristic p, and let F be the subfield of p elements (see Exercise 9, Chapter 4). Show that, considered as a vector space over F, K has finite dimension n, say, and that the number of elements in K is then p^n.

12. If $f(x)$ is an irreducible polynomial over $\mathbf{J}_p$ (p prime) of degree n, show that $\mathbf{J}_p[x]/(f(x))$ is a field with p^n elements.

13. Show that $f(x) = x^3 + x + 1$ is irreducible over $\mathbf{J}_2$. Find the eight elements of the field $\mathbf{J}_2[x]/(f(x))$, and give the addition and multiplication tables.

14. Given two points O and A in the plane, show that it is impossible by a finite number of ruler-and-compasses constructions to obtain a point B such that $OB^3 = 2\ OA^3$. (This shows that, given a cube whose side has length OA, it is impossible to construct the length OB which is the side of a cube with twice the volume of the original cube.)

15. Prove that a regular 9-sided polygon and a regular 18-sided polygon are not constructible with ruler and compasses. [Hint: Use Theorem 76.]

Answers to the Exercises

Chapter One. 1. (i) No, (ii) No, (iii) Yes, (iv) Yes.

2. Let $\mathbf{O} = \begin{pmatrix} 0 & 0 \\ 0 & 0 \end{pmatrix}$, $\mathbf{I} = \begin{pmatrix} 1 & 0 \\ 0 & 1 \end{pmatrix}$, $\mathbf{A} = \begin{pmatrix} 0 & 1 \\ 1 & 0 \end{pmatrix}$, $\mathbf{B} = \begin{pmatrix} 1 & 1 \\ 1 & 1 \end{pmatrix}$.

+	O	I	A	B
O	O	I	A	B
I	I	O	B	A
A	A	B	O	I
B	B	A	I	O

×	O	I	A	B
O	O	O	O	O
I	O	I	A	B
A	O	A	I	B
B	O	B	B	O

1, 2, 3, 4, 5, 6, 7, 8 are satisfied.

5.

+	0	1	2	3	4
0	0	1	2	3	4
1	1	2	3	4	0
2	2	3	4	0	1
3	3	4	0	1	2
4	4	0	1	2	3

×	0	1	2	3	4
0	0	0	0	0	0
1	0	1	2	3	4
2	0	2	4	1	3
3	0	3	1	4	2
4	0	4	3	2	1

The solution of the equation is $x = 4$.

7.

+	0	1	2	3	4	5
0	0	1	2	3	4	5
1	1	2	3	4	5	0
2	2	3	4	5	0	1
3	3	4	5	0	1	2
4	4	5	0	1	2	3
5	5	0	1	2	3	4

×	0	1	2	3	4	5
0	0	0	0	0	0	0
1	0	1	2	3	4	5
2	0	2	4	0	2	4
3	0	3	0	3	0	3
4	0	4	2	0	4	2
5	0	5	4	3	2	1

(i) $x = 2$ or 5, (ii) none, (iii) $x = 1$ or 3, (iv) none.
8. In J_{10}: 2, 4, 6, 8. In J_{12}: 2, 3, 4, 6, 8, 9, 10.

ANSWERS TO EXERCISES

Chapter Three. 3. 3, 5, 7, 11, 13, 17, 19, 23, 29, 31, 37, 41, 43, 47, 53, 59, 61, 67, 71, 73, 79, 83, 89, 97.

4. 2, 3; 2, 5; 2, 7; 2, 9; 3, 4; 3, 5; 3, 7; 3, 8; 4, 5; 4, 7; 4, 9; 5, 6; 5, 7; 5, 8; 5, 9; 6, 7; 7, 8; 7, 9; 8, 9.

11. (i) $19 = 2a - 3b$, (ii) $21 = -15a + 38b$.

12. $s = 4, t = -11$.

Chapter Five. 1. $ac + ad + bc + bd$.

5. The zero is -1, the identity is 0.

7. The ideals U are $\{0\}$, $\{0, 6\}$, $\{0, 4, 8\}$, $\{0, 3, 6, 9\}$, $\{0, 2, 4, 6, 8, 10\}$, $\mathbf{J}_{12}$. The quotient rings $\mathbf{J}_{12}/U$ are isomorphic to $\mathbf{J}_{12}$, $\mathbf{J}_6$, $\mathbf{J}_4$, $\mathbf{J}_3$, $\mathbf{J}_2$, $\{0\}$ respectively.

8. The elements of R/U are the cosets [0], [2], [4], [6]. The brackets are omitted in the tables:

+	0	2	4	6
0	0	2	4	6
2	2	4	6	0
4	4	6	0	2
6	6	0	2	4

×	0	2	4	6
0	0	0	0	0
2	0	4	0	4
4	0	0	0	0
6	0	4	0	4

R/U is not isomorphic to $\mathbf{J}_4$.

9. $\{0, 3, 6, 9\}$, $\{0, 2, 4, 6, 8, 10\}$.

14. No.

17. $\phi(0) = 0$, $\phi(2) = 2$, $\phi(4) = 4$, $\phi(6) = 1$, $\phi(8) = 3$.

Chapter Six. 2. In $\mathbf{J}_6$: 1, 5. In $\mathbf{J}_7$: 1, 2, 3, 4, 5, 6. In $\mathbf{J}_8$: 1, 3, 5, 7.

5. $\pm 1 \pm i$.

6. $(1 + 2i)(2 - i)$, $(2 + i)(2 - i)$, $(1 - 2i)(-1 + i)$.

7. $(2 + \sqrt{2})(3 - \sqrt{2})$, $(10 + 7\sqrt{2})(10 - 7\sqrt{2})$, $1 + 2\sqrt{2}$.

8. $3.7 = (1 + 2\sqrt{(-5)})(1 - 2\sqrt{(-5)})$, $2.7 = (2 + \sqrt{(-5)})(2 - \sqrt{(-5)})$.

10. $q(x) = x^2 + x - 1, r(x) = 4x + 2$.

11. $x^2 - 2x + 1 = -\frac{1}{3}(x - 2)a(x) + \frac{1}{3}(x - 1)b(x)$.

12. $x - 2i$.

13. (i) $(x + 1)(x + 2)(x + 3)(x + 4)$, (ii) $(x + 2)(x + 5)$, (iii) $(x^2 + 1)$, (iv) $(x + 7)(x^2 + 4x + 5)$.

14. $x^2 + x + 1$, $x^3 + x^2 + 1$, $x^3 + x + 1$.

16. $3(x^2 - 5x + 2)$, $1(-x^2 - 2x - 1)$, $\frac{1}{4}(x^2 - 3x + 2)$, $\frac{3}{2}(-3x^2 - 5x + 2)$.

ANSWERS TO EXERCISES

Chapter Seven. 3. (i) 1.d., (ii) 1.i., (iii) 1.i., (iv) 1.d.

4. Fields of characteristic 2.

7. $\frac{1}{6}$, $\frac{1}{6}$, $\frac{2}{3}$; -1, 1, 1.

8. 0, 0, 1, -2; 1, 0, -1, 2; 0, 1, 0, $-\frac{1}{2}$; 0, 0, 0, $\frac{1}{2}$.

10. Ker $\phi = \{\xi \mid \phi(\xi) = 0\}$. Im $\phi = \{\eta \mid \phi(\xi) = \eta$, for some ξ in $V\}$. ϕ is an isomorphism if Ker $\phi = \{0\}$ and Im $\phi = V'$.

Chapter Eight. 3. $x^4 - 4x^2 + 16$, $x^4 - 10x^2 + 23$, $x^4 - x^2 - \frac{19}{4}$.

7. $\frac{4}{5} + \frac{1}{5}\theta^2$.

8. $\frac{1}{3} - \frac{1}{3} 2^{1/3} + \frac{1}{3} 2^{2/3}$.

13. The elements are 0, 1, $x = a$ (say), $x + 1 = b$, $x^2 = c$, $x^2 + 1 = d$, $x^2 + x = e$, $x^2 + x + 1 = f$.

+	0	1	a	b	c	d	e	f
0	0	1	a	b	c	d	e	f
1	1	0	b	a	d	c	f	e
a	a	b	0	1	e	f	c	d
b	b	a	1	0	f	e	d	c
c	c	d	e	f	0	1	a	b
d	d	c	f	e	1	0	b	a
e	e	f	c	d	a	b	0	1
f	f	e	d	c	b	a	1	0

×	0	1	a	b	c	d	e	f
0	0	0	0	0	0	0	0	0
1	0	1	a	b	c	d	e	f
a	0	a	c	e	b	1	f	d
b	0	b	e	d	f	c	1	a
c	0	c	b	f	e	a	d	1
d	0	d	1	c	a	f	b	e
e	0	e	f	1	d	b	a	c
f	0	f	d	a	1	e	c	b

Index

INDEX

INDEX

Theorem 18 page 18.

Example: $7\overline{)39}$ $=$ a $= bq + r$

$39 = 7.5 + 4$

S is the set $\mathbb{Z}^+ : s \in \mathbb{Z}^+ \cap S = a - bk$

$k = 1, 2, 3, 4, 5$ $= 39 - 7k$

$\therefore S = \left\{ 32, 25, 18, 11, 4 \right\}$

Let r be the smallest element $s \in S$. ie $s = 4$

and let $r = a - bq$ say and $r > 0$

Moreover $r < b$, for if $r = b$ then $a = b(q+1)$ & if
$r > b$ then $a - b(q+1)$ is an element of S smaller than r

$r > b$

$a - bq > b$ ie $a - bq - b > 0$

$\therefore s = a - b(q+1) > 0$

$\therefore s - r < 0$ since $a - b(q+1) - (a - bq) = -b < 0$ by def^n
$s < r$